CREATING LUXURIOUS

SWIMMING

POOLS

BY JACK HARDING

Published by Elliot Press Ltd

Copyright © Jack Harding
Published 2014

ISBN: 978-0-9927890-0-8

ELLIOT   PRESS

contents

acknowledgements

Acres Wild - enquiries@acreswild.co.uk
Adrian James & Darren Riddle - www.adrianjames.com
Alex Durtnell @ R Durtnell & Sons Ltd
- www.durtnell.co.uk
Anthony Paul Landscape Design
- www.anthonypaullandscapedesign.com
Arne Maynard - www.arnemaynard.com
Barr & Wray - www.barrandwray.com
Base Contracts - www.basecontracts.com
Bob Whiteway
Brian Herbert @ Outdoor Options
- www.outdooroptions.co.uk
Bruce Harding
Cheesmur Builders - www.cheesmur.co.uk
Dan Backshell
Derek & Clinton Chapman
Douglas Briggs Associates
- www.douglasbriggspartnership.co.uk
Eddie McAtominey
Fairwater - info@fairwater.co.uk
Glyn Lucas @ DG Pools & Leisure - www.dgpools.co.uk
GMD - www.gmdevelopments.co.uk
Gordon & Tom Smith
Graham & David Brough
Graham Varney - www.benfieldandloxley.co.uk
Guncast Team - www.guncast.com
Haka Designs - info@hakadesigns.com

Hann Tucker Associates - www.hanntucker.co.uk
Ian Adam Smith - www.ianadam-smith.co.uk
Ian Laurence @ F3 Architects - www.f3architects.co.uk
ISO Energy - www.isoenergy.co.uk
James Rae/Duncan Baker-Brown
@ BBM Sustainable Design - www.bbm-architects.co.uk
John France - jfrance@lifestyleprojects.com
Limewood Hotel - www.limewoodhotel.co.uk
Mark Robinson @ Robinson Associates
- robinsonengineers.co.uk
Martin Goodey & Andy Gale
Martyn Arrowsmith
Meadowcroft Griffin Architects
- www.meadowcroftgriffin.co.uk
Michalis Boyd Architects - www.michalisboyd.com
Mike Wiseman @ Basements Design
- www.basementdesignstudio.co.uk
Milk Architecture & Design Ltd - www.spashofmilk.com
Nick Handslip
Nik & Katie Webb @ Molokini Marketing Ltd
- www.molokini.co.uk
OMK - www.omk-design.co.uk
Paul Carter @ WG Carter Ltd - enquiries@wgcarter.co.uk
Paul Green @ Green County Developments
- www.gcdltd.com
Paul Howlett & Dan Maloney
Peter Kent @ FT Allen - www.ftallen.co.uk

Peter Mercieca - Kodiak Construction Ltd
Phillip Acton @ Phillips Chartered Surveyors
- www.philipscharteredsurveyors.co.uk
Pip Morrison & Mary Keen Landscape Architect -
pipmorrison@yahoo.co.uk
Purple Dragon - www.purpledragonplay.com
Ray Thompson - info@thompsonbaroni.com
Reed Harris - www.reedharris.co.uk
Richard Holden & Andrew Harper @ Holden Harper
- www.holdenharper.co.uk
Richard Wilch
Rob Coulson @ Symm - www.symm.co.uk
Robert Irving (Photographer) - www.robirving.com
Scott Guest @ Atlas Refurbishment
- www.atlasrefurb.co.uk
Simon Morray-Jones and Neil Etheridge @ SMJ Architects
- www.sm-j.com
Steve French & Martyn Arrowsmith
Stuart Pearson @ RW Armstrong
- www.rwarmstrong.co.uk
Stuart Whittaker @ ARC Construction
- www.arcconstruct.com
Teemu Griffiths
White Horse Electrical

suppliers

Suppliers: Sika - gbr.sika.com; Sealocrete - www.sealocrete.com; Bisazza - www.bisazza.com; Trend - www.tiles.org.uk; Marbelite - www.marbelite.com; Mapei - www.mapei.com; Artisans - www.artisansofdevizes.com; Stone Age - www.stones-age.co.uk; SPATA - www.spata.co.uk; PWTAG - www.pwtag.org; HSE Managing Health & Safety - www.hse.gov.uk; Ardex - www.ardex.co.uk; Fluvo -www.certikin.co.uk; Triogen - www.triogen.co.uk; Bayrol - www.bayrol.com; Certikin - www.certikin.co.uk; ASTRAL - www.astralpooluk.com; DROM - www.dromuk.com; RIW - www.riw.co.uk; Pool Filtration - www.poolfiltration.com; Fastlane - www.certikin.co.uk; Hydro Air Jets - www.certikin.co.uk; and Garth Marnoch @ Stonegres - Garth@stonegres.co.uk.

All images used in this book feature pools built by Guncast

foreword

I am Jack Harding and I have spent my working life constructing swimming pools, mainly within the British Isles and mainland Europe and, on occasion, further afield.

My career began in the early 1990's when I left college and started working with my father, Bruce, who managed and operated a company called Guncast Swimming Pools. Guncast's origins trace back to the 1970's and following my father's retirement in 2000, I am now the managing director.

Guncast is a well known swimming pool brand that specialises in the construction of very high quality commercial and domestic swimming pools. Guncast is one of the larger, longer established swimming pool construction companies based in Britain today, with offices in Belgium and New York.

By definition and by experience of personally overseeing and building many high specification, luxury swimming pools, I suppose you could say that I am a swimming pool expert, which has led me to write this book.

ABOUT THIS BOOK

In my office I maintain a library of swimming pool books, literature and journals which I use regularly for technical reference and, of course, for inspiration. Few however combine the 'technical' with 'inspirational'.

My desire and aim in writing this book was to combine the two and create a book in which the layman, or indeed professional, can find inspiration for their swimming pool project, but in the same book have useful, practical guidance in the technical aspects of installation.

In the following chapters, I will use examples of swimming pools, constructed by our company, that are either complicated, interesting or inspiring. They are shown with, of course, the owners' permission but we decided that the location and name of the owner should not be revealed.

Each chapter is themed and features inspiring photographs supported by the technical ins and outs to help the reader understand the planning and design needed to create a very beautiful and unique swimming pool.

This book is dedicated to my father, Bruce Harding.

introduction

HISTORY OF SWIMMING POOLS

We are all aware that swimming pools have existed since Roman Times, and some historical data indicates that public pools may have existed well before this in other civilisations around the world.

The world is mostly covered by water, and humankind is intrinsically linked to it, with a natural desire to swim and bathe. I believe that swimming and bathing, whether in the sea, natural pools, lakes, thermal pools, or indeed man-made swimming pools, is something human beings enjoy doing and consider a luxury.

It is logical to conclude that, if money or space were no object, to own a private swimming pool has become an aspiration for most of us.

Private swimming pools were of course built pre 1960, but it is only really after this date that the proliferation of private swimming pools began, particularly in Europe, USA and Australia.

Demand now spans the world, with many hundreds of thousands being built annually and in some regions, it might even be considered abnormal for the property not to have a swimming pool in the grounds or garden. You only have to look out of an airplane window when landing in destinations such as Nice, France, to see how true this is.

chapter 1

'CONSTRUCTION METHODS'

This mass market for private swimming pools needed methods of construction that were cost efficient to enable mass sales.

It was during the early period of swimming pool construction for the private client that the liner pool, fibreglass pool and concrete tiled pool were tailored for the private market. These techniques are still used today to construct swimming pools as new construction technology has either not been successful or not forthcoming.

Clients' demands have moved on, bringing new technologies such as moving floor pools and filtration techniques. There have also been dramatic improvements to the standard of finish in the twenty first century, compared to the blue rectangular or kidney shaped pools of the 1970's and 1980's.

However, the base construction methods are still typically the same. In the chapters that follow we will describe and detail these modern high specification swimming pools, but will illustrate within this introduction the various different swimming pool construction methods, finishing options and filtration and sterilisation techniques.

LINER POOLS

A liner pool has a blockwork, aluminium or pre insulated (against heat loss) frame or structure which is subsequently lined internally with a PVC (polyvinyl chloride) plastic liner. The liner is patterned or coloured and has the dual purpose of being the waterproof membrane as well as the finish of the swimming pool itself.

There are a number of standards and qualities of liner available, with the highest quality being the on site welded liner, which is very durable and more robust than the standard one piece liner (affectionately known as the 'bag' liner). The welded liner is cut into sections on site and is therefore more versatile in terms of the shape that can be achieved. This has been particularly important as customers' aspirations have changed throughout the years.

In the UK, particularly during the 1980's, the liner pool was by far the most common installation, being quick to install and therefore less costly. The customer could theoretically order a liner pool at Easter and be swimming by the summer. However, over the years, for one reason or another, they have become less popular, probably due to market evolution or changes in customer behaviour.

Liners or welded liners are often used in the refurbishment market for lining old concrete pools that are cracked, leaking or soiled. They have a life span of between seven and twenty years, after which a liner replacement needs undertaking as it can become stretched, wrinkled and/or faded over time and, of course, if they are pierced anywhere they would need patching.

Oxford Pool Building Company (now owned by Guncast) was peaking during the 1980's at installing eighty 'bag' liner pools per year. The company now installs less than a dozen per year and most of these are of the on site welded type.

FIBREGLASS POOLS

One, or even multi-piece, fibreglass pools are pre-fabricated and delivered to site on a large lorry and then craned into a pre-excavated hole.

Occasionally the fibreglass pool can be ordered with an internal mosaic or tile lining, with the mosaic pre-adhered directly onto the fibreglass. This is more commonly seen on the smaller fibreglass hydro spa pools, which can be pre-tiled to match a wider scheme or an adjacent pool but have the advantage of the spa being 'dropped in' on site, rather than having to be constructed on site.

Like the liner pool, the fibreglass pool is also the finish and waterproof membrane. The large majority of 'off the shelf' fibreglass pools are blue and can be seen for sale on the side of the road in garden centres in France.

On site fibreglass lining to existing pools is also undertaken, often where a concrete pool has passed into disrepair and needs a new lease of life and refurbishment. Similar to liner pools, fibreglass pools are generally less costly, mainly because they are much quicker to construct on site and therefore, less labour intensive. The components are also mass produced off site.

STAINLESS STEEL POOLS

Stainless steel swimming pools can be one piece or welded together on site. Similar to the fibreglass pool, the stainless steel becomes the finish as well as the waterproof membrane.

Stainless steel pools are considered to be one of the most watertight and durable swimming pools available. They are also extremely striking to look at, often installed on boutique hotel rooftops for example, where a lightweight structure is of huge importance.

However, even a small stainless steel pool is very expensive and could easily be ten times the cost of a similar sized liner pool. The stainless steel swimming pool market is therefore, by comparison, very small throughout the world, but even so, there are a number a quality companies that do specialise in this market.

CONCRETE POOLS

Concrete swimming pools are formed from either reinforced concrete blockwork, sprayed reinforced concrete (known as shotcrete or gunite - hence the Guncast brand name), or shuttered and poured reinforced concrete.

These are all usually waterproof rendered or lined with a cementitious waterproof membrane. A finish is then adhered to the rendered surface such as mosaic, large format ceramic or porcelain tiles, or a plaster type applied finish such as marbelite. The pros and cons of these constructional methods are as outlined below.

CONCRETE BLOCKWORK POOLS

The blockwork pool is the less expensive to construct of the three systems and can be formed by a good quality traditional builder, as well as a specialist swimming pool company. The system comprises of a reinforced concrete slab in an excavated hole, with steel starter bars that protrude up from the concrete slab and through the centre of each block, which is subsequently tied onto a horizontal reinforcing rod. The hollow in each block is then poured with concrete to give the pool walls their design strength.

This style of construction is usually formed with a hopper shaped deep end to the pool, as the block walls have a limitation on depth. Also, clearly by virtue of being block work, they are most suited to rectangular pools.

One inherent problem with blockwork pools is that they rely on skilled labour to ensure that the concrete being poured into the hollow blocks makes its way right to the bottom. When one is working 'blind' it is often difficult to get the concrete all the way to the deepest part of the hollows in the block - leaving a void in the structure when the concrete hardens, which is inevitably a weak point. This is often the reason that older block pools develop leaks or cracks and are quite problematic to repair in a cost efficient way.

The blockwork pool is most commonly seen only in the domestic sector. Structural engineers generally specify that sprayed reinforced concrete, or shuttered and poured reinforced concrete, is used in the construction of commercially used swimming pools, which are seen to be more robust.

SPRAYED CONCRETE - GUNITE AND SHOTCRETE

To form a sprayed concrete swimming pool shell, a one sided shutter is formed with lightweight timber to external walls of the swimming pool to the design shape, within the excavation. The shutter is then lined with steelwork to the specifying engineer's design and the concrete applied pneumatically under pressure via a 50mm spray nozzle.

The skilled "nozzle man" applies the concrete in layers, building the pool shell up. The concrete is either hand batched on site and the sand and cement loaded through a hopper to the delivery hose, (gunite or dry method) or the concrete is delivered ready mixed in lorries and, again, loaded through a hopper (shotcrete or wet method).

Both methods produce a very hard monolithic reinforced concrete structure to any shape, depth or design, as the concrete is applied under pressure making it dense.

As the application process requires far less shuttering when compared to a fully shuttered and poured swimming pool shell, this type of construction tends to be less expensive than the shuttered pool, but requires more specialist plant and very skilled labour. Therefore, it is more expensive than the block pool.

This is the method of swimming pool shell (structural shell) that Guncast has most commonly used to build swimming pools.

SHUTTERED AND POURED

Shuttered and poured swimming pools are formed fully in the shutter with the fixed steelwork within. The concrete is then poured into the shutter and vibrated with a special vibrating poker to give the concrete density. Often the swimming pool shell is poured in sections and pieced together over days and weeks. The joints between the various slabs of concrete are linked using 'waterbars', which are rubber barriers inset into each slab of concrete to provide a waterproof link between the two.

When fitted correctly, waterbars do ultimately seal the joints and a waterproof concrete box is formed. As the independent slabs of concrete are liable to movement, a flexible joint has to appear between the tiled finish within the pool tank, which is not ideal for more aesthetically demanding projects. This type of construction method is often seen on the larger projects or municipal pools, where the pool tank is actually formed within, or as part of, the overall structure of the building that the pool is sited in. Shuttered and poured pools are at the top end of the cost spectrum for building the pool structure.

FUTURE CONSTRUCTION METHODS

The construction methods described above have remained largely unchanged since the 1970's.

Now and again I have seen brick built pools which tend to be very old and, during the 1960's, there was a system called "hand pack" pre-sprayed concrete, where an excavated hole was lined with steel and a ready mix concrete vehicle would unload its concrete into the hole as labourers shovelled it up the walls to form the tank.

As we progress into the future, energy saving becomes more and more of an issue:

> "In 2011 the UK government included swimming pools in Part L building regulations which stipulate insulative standards or 'U' values."

We see pre-insulated swimming panel systems becoming available on the market, which can have a liner fitted and permanent systems of shuttering. These can be used for concrete pool construction providing insulation as required. For example, 100mm thick interlocking extruded polystyrene sheets that clip together can then be sprayed with concrete on top.

As systems of construction become refined, there are of course nuances between the way we used to do things and the way we will do things in the future. However, the principal methods of swimming pool construction described are with us for the foreseeable future.

Generally, it is the concrete pool that is rendered then tiled. However, there are so many different tiles, mosaic, natural stone and myriad other products that have been used or are being used to line this type of swimming pool, that the modern day choices for finish are vast.

Designers and architects continue to push boundaries and since the beginning of the twenty first century, some of the most visually stunning swimming pools have been created using bespoke finishing materials.

Since this time, the typical blue mosaic pool is rarely seen as a new build. Pools are being designed into their surroundings and environs using slate, limestone, porcelain tiles, glass mosaic, coloured render and marbelite – with very successful results.

As these bespoke pools have become more and more common, then of course the customers have become more and more aesthetically demanding.

chapter 2

'FINISHING OPTIONS'

By far the most important aspect of the swimming pool project to any client, whether private or commercial, is aesthetics. The way the pool will look is the primary concern and focus and, whilst functionality and performance are obviously important, it is the final appearance of the swimming pool that excites the large proportion of individuals, designers or companies involved.

As outlined in the previous chapter, when it comes to choosing a finish or lining for a swimming pool, there are two types of swimming pool.

Firstly, there is the swimming pool where the structure or waterproof membrane is the finish or lining itself. The choice of internal lining is limited only by the number of patterns or colours available from a supplier. Similarly, most fibreglass pools have a blue finish, but a small selection of other colours such as grey or white are available. A stainless steel finish is desirable and often seen in the most chic swimming pool installations. Exceptions to this are the fibreglass or stainless steel pools which are then tiled or painted. Although uncommon, I have seen a stainless steel swimming pool with a spray painted surface in Switzerland.

The other category is the swimming pool that is constructed then lined.

POOL COPING OR EDGING

It is the modus operandi of all pool finishers to lay the perimeter stone coping or tiled edge to the swimming pool as their first job. It is usual that the first row of edging stone around the outdoor pool (known as coping) is the swimming pool contractor's responsibility and, for an indoor swimming pool, the first course of tiling is the pool edge.

The reason the swimming pool finisher beds the pool coping or adheres the pool edge tile first, is that it gives the level for the swimming pool and also gives the finisher an edge to work the pool render to.

In short, the coping or edging sets out the pool, which of course is critical as water is level, and if the pool is not exactly level it will show. The responsibility for getting this correct falls into the swimming pool contractor's domain and is that is why this first course of tiling or edging is often part of the pool construction package.

Once the pool edge is set and the tile or coping laid, the landscaper laying paving around the pool or the surround tiler can lay away from the pool and everything should dovetail in to the correct levels.

There are exceptions to this rule. In some instances the pool coping is specially formed by a stone mason and this type of work can be lengthy from instruction to completion. Sometimes a pool is therefore pre-tiled prior to the pool coping being delivered to site. In these cases the pool finisher will erect a batten in place of the coping or tile and work to this; then remove the batten and tile the pool perimeter last of all.

Some pools are 'deck level' or 'infinity edge', which involves a method of filtering the pool water that is detailed later on. Again, because levels are so critical, it is the pool contractor's responsibility and the finisher's task to tile this detail. The most common tiling arrangement for this detail is a submerged coping or tile on the immediate edge of the pool.

Below, there is a collection gully (which if open, would definitely also be tiled), under a grate or 'deck level grate' (which could be white or coloured PVC, stainless steel, natural stone or even wood – and is supplied and set in as part of the pool contract). Then there is a backing stone or tile, like the single perimeter coping or tile, which the landscaper or surround tiler works up to.

Obviously there are plenty of competent swimming pool contractors who may also offer the surrounding hard landscaping, or even construction of the pool hall, in which case, their pool tiler would probably complete the surround tiling as well. Generally the coping or edge tile inward is considered to be the swimming pool builder's work.

For indoor swimming pools there are a range of edge tiles that have rounded edges.

A common material would be ceramic and size would be something in the order of 240mm x 120mm x 8mm thick. Standards are beige or white and, for more commercial applications, these are ribbed and have a defined edge in a contrasting colour.

Generally the falls on an indoor swimming pool surround are back toward the pool and, therefore, the perimeter edge tile is also laid slightly toward the pool, hence these tiles are flat and do not have the raised profile seen on external pool man-made copings.

For more bespoke and luxurious pools, natural stone can be fashioned into an edge tile to match the surround tile, or recent advances in porcelain fabrication have enabled porcelain to be formed onto square or round edge tiles.

Natural stone has a chequered history when used within the pool environment as it is known that pool water can cause natural stones to delaminate, scale, discolour or erode. As an alternative, porcelain can look equally stunning and this man-made material offers a reliable substitute to natural stone, such as limestone and slate.

For outdoor swimming pools there are off-the-shelf reconstituted marble chipping profiled edging stones, available in white or buff colour.

Again, natural stone can be fashioned to form edging stones that can match the surround paving. For the outdoor environment, tried and tested external paving such as Yorkstone is fine for the surround and coping. In contrast, it is more complicated installing natural stone within a pool hall where the temperature and humidity is high.

Outdoor pool copings can be flat but need to be laid away from the pool; otherwise they are profiled to throw the water away from the pool.

The coping or edge tile is pointed with mortar or grouted in the normal way.

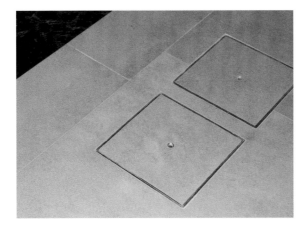

WATERPROOF RENDERING

In the early years of marbelite swimming pools, this particular lining was, in some cases, deemed to be of sufficient waterproof integrity that it was applied as both the finish and waterproof lining. For concrete pools, using this finish as waterproof is uncommon and today, in nearly all cases, the concrete swimming pool is 'waterproof rendered'.

Waterproof rendering is a system using a mortar of sand and cement (preferably coarse sand which gives body or strength to the mix), mixed with a waterproofing additive. Waterproof additives are supplied via all builders merchants and common brand names include Sika or Sealocrete.

The waterproof rendering system comprises an initial 'splatter coat' with SBR additive, a waterproof bonding agent, then two further layers of render with waterproof additive. Water does not tend to leak through the pool structure itself as long as it is formed properly. However, water does have a propensity to leak through natural joints in the concrete structure or around pool fittings such as light inlets which, being made from different materials such as PVC or stainless steel, do not bond well with concrete.

It is, therefore, these areas that the experienced 'pool finisher', a very skilled operative not only in waterproof rendering but also in quality tiling and mosaic art, will pay particular attention to. It is good practice for the pool construction team to leave cut outs or dish around pool fittings or lights to allow the pool finisher to pack in waterproof render to these areas in order to prevent leaking around pool fittings. There are also expansion strips that can be taped around pool fittings, which expand on contact with water (hydrophilic strip) to enhance the water tightness in these areas.

To get a swimming pool 100% water tight is very difficult to achieve and, as a result, there are permissible rates of water loss through a swimming pool structure. In any pool installation where water egress is a potential issue, for example a first storey swimming pool, it is best to assume from the onset that some minimal leakage is to be expected. Therefore, a drainage collection system would be fitted to deal with this water and avoid build up.

RENDER OR MARBELITE FINISH POOLS

Once a pool is rendered, it can then be tiled or finished with one of the following options:

A white cement paste impregnated with marble chippings and marble dust was commonly used during the 1970's as a swimming pool lining and known as marbelite or marbeline. The concrete pool was formed and either waterproof rendered or left as bare concrete, then the marbelite was trowelled onto the pool walls to form a hard white permanent pool lining. Thousands of swimming pools were finished this way, most often in America and the UK, and can still be seen today. This type of lining was sold as the cheaper alternative to a fully tiled swimming pool.

Similar to pool liners, a marbelite lining does not have an infinite life span as the cement or bonding agent will erode over time, leaving the surface pitted. It is also susceptible to staining. Consequently whilst thousands of pools of this type were built in the 1970's, thousands were refurbished in the 1990's and 2000's.

In recent years, marbelite has had a bit of a renaissance as colouring or dyeing the marbelite has been used to produce a seamless lining to the pool. By blending dyes, almost any colour variant can be achieved. This is very appealing to pool owners and designers as it enables them to create their own uniquely coloured swimming pool.

Pre-1970's and pre-marbelite, many pools were rendered then painted with a chlorinated rubber pool paint, typically in blue, light blue or white. With the advent of marbelite, and the fact that the painted pools (like woodwork) need periodically repainting, these are very rare these days and it would be unusual to construct a pool this way now.

An alternative to the 'plaster' type finish pool is render or coloured render. With dyes the render can be coloured or treated to achieve a look similar to marbelite. However, day joints between continuity of work, crazing (in the render) and differences in sand and cement batching, make this very difficult to exact and the end product is not flawless. Whilst some people like the 'antique' look, it is not to everyone's taste and, again, not a commonly seen finish.

MOSAIC

Since Roman times, mosaic has been used to create the most resplendent floor and wall finishes and can be seen on old Roman villa floors and, in modern times, in luxury hotel bathrooms and hotel foyers.

The other mass use of mosaic over the last forty years has been to line swimming pools. A multitude of colours and a variety of textures or copper veins within the tile material itself allows the mosaic artist to create murals, patterns, artwork and colour schemes with limitless effect. Of course the blue mosaic is synonymous with swimming pools but over the last four decades virtually all colours have been used and countless motifs, floor patterns and murals laid into pools.

There are two mainstream types of mosaic.

GLASS MOSAIC

Historically produced in Italy, glass mosaic is now also produced in countries such as France and China. However, 'Italian glass mosaic' is still the 'big name' in this industry and is the most sought after.

The glass mosaic arrives pre-adhered to sheets of mesh which are then attached onto the adhesive bed. An alternative is paperface mosaic where paper is glued onto the front of the mosaic and the rear is pushed into the adhesive bed with the paper subsequently washed off.

The sheet sizes are usually around 300mm by 300mm and the mosaic itself is normally about 20mm by 20mm by 2-3mm, with 2mm grout joints. Other sizes are available, but the vast majority are this size.

The individual mosaics are formed from vitreous glass and each have a certain uniqueness about them. Being glass they are transparent to a degree (especially the lighter colours), which is important because the colour of the adhesive bed and substrate could affect the appearance of the mosaics.

CERAMIC MOSAIC

Supplied on both paper and mesh in the same way glass mosaic is and on a similar sheet size, the mosaics themselves are mostly 25mm x 25mm and thicker than the glass mosaic at 4-5mm. Ceramic mosaic is more widely available than glass and derives from countries such as Spain, Japan and Malaysia. The ceramic tile is glazed and, like the glass mosaic, there are a huge range of colours available.

It is preferred that paper face mosaics are used for swimming pool tiling as this guarantees full adhesion to the rear of the mosaic. The mesh system can prevent full adhesion as the mesh gets in the way. Also some mesh is glued to the mosaic with soluble glue (not suitable for use in a swimming pool) and this layer of glue can also prevent full adhesion.

LAYING MOSAIC TILES

Once the mosaic is adhered onto the pool structure, it is grouted, typically using white or grey grouts. There is a range of coloured grouts available from companies such as Mapei, who also makes an epoxy grout that has the benefit of being a chemical composite, which is impervious to water and more consistent in colour than the cementitious grouts.

The epoxy grout range is more expensive and much more labour intensive to lay. This is because as it is laid the residue has to be immediately removed using special sponges otherwise it will be seen on the tile itself. Alternatively, using the same dye that is used for the coloured render process, the base cementitious grout can be dyed to virtually any colour or shade (by blending two dye colours).

The dye that is needed for this process has to be chlorine and UV (light) resistant and is extremely expensive. It can only be bought in bulk from wholesale suppliers. Dyes supplied on the high street are not suitable, as they are not UV or chlorine resistent. The benefit this process offers is that the pool finisher can achieve any colour to match the tile or mosaic by blending, and can dye the adhesive to the same shade, which is very advantageous when using the more transparent glass mosaic.

With mosaic, especially the thinner glass mosaic, it is essential that if the underlying adhesive is a different colour, it is scraped back to ensure none of the adhesive pokes through the grout – which will result in patchy grouting between the mosaic tiles.

This is quite a common problem as scraping back the adhesive in this way is an intensely tedious process and short cuts can be tempting. Furthermore, when working with white adhesive and a beige grout, for example, while the difference is very difficult to see in the dry, when the grout is submerged the difference becomes very clear.

NATURAL STONE

A more exclusive internal lining to a swimming pool would be natural stone; in particular slate or limestone, although marble and other types of stone have been used.

The natural beauty of these products is appealing and the ability to run the surround stone into the coping and down into the pool attracts the discerning designer. However the selection of natural stone for swimming pool use is fraught with problems, as previously mentioned.

Paradoxically, indoor pools live in relatively aggressive environments where humidity, heat and splash can stain, scale or spoil pool surround stone work. The outdoor pool surround is much more suited to natural stone as this is the environment from where the stone was originally sourced.

Natural stone within the pool itself is even more prone to problems, especially in cases where the stone itself is not dense and will absorb the pool water.

Natural stone is inclined to scale (which becomes more likely the warmer the pool water) or stain and discolour as the pool water gets drawn in. Poorer quality stone can delaminate or erode. There is a small handful of very high end specialist stone suppliers in the UK who, by rigorous testing, have small parcels of natural stone suitable for swimming pool use, but even these will age (some people like the effect) unlike man-made products.

PORCELAIN

This of course leads onto the man-made alternative to natural stone, which really is porcelain. Porcelain is available in a range of textures and sizes, and can be shaped to look like, for example, a chunky coping stone.

The colours and textures are typically intended to mimic natural stones and slates and, broadly speaking, they are very good. Obviously side by side with natural stone, the difference can be seen, but on its own the impression is right.

Porcelain can be pre-cut to any size, from the largest pieces generally being 1200mm by 1200mm. Porcelain is incredibly durable and resistant to absorption, staining, scaling and delamination. It is a good quality product for use in swimming pools.

More salubrious and exotic finishes would include natural shell mosaic, gold or silver clad mosaic, onyx and marbles. All these are extremely expensive and, given the cost of removing or replacing with a more tried and tested product if something like this were to fail, one needs to make absolutely sure they are in harmony with swimming pool water prior to installing.

On the more municipal swimming pool, large format ceramic white or blue tiles are often used – typically 240mm x 120mm x 10mm with epoxy grouting, and wider flexible joints over the expansion joints (the jointing within the concrete). In fact, this type of tiling is termed 'large format tiling'. It is rare to see this fitted to domestic pools.

chapter 3

'FILTRATION AND DISINFECTION SYSTEMS'

Indoor swimming pools and outdoor swimming pools, commercial or domestic, are all filtered and disinfected using a range of systems, but the principal is always the same. The water is filtered through a filter tank with filter media and then treated or disinfected with something like chlorine. It is then nearly always heated (see next chapter).

SKIMMERS

The pool water is drawn off from the pool via surface skimmers, which are pool side units, usually white PVC, that 'skim' airborne debris from the pool water surface and 'suck' in leaves and debris. The number of units will depend on the size of the pool as well as the capability of the filtration system. The pump and filter sizing needs to be powerful enough to drive each of these skimmers.

Each skimmer unit has an accessible lid through the pool side paving or tiling. The pool will also draw water from 'pool sumps' which should be sited at the deepest point of the pool and should always be at least in pairs and a minimum of 2m apart to avoid entrapment (e.g. bathers being 'sucked' in and not being able to release themselves). The science behind this is that one sump blocked will ensure the pool water is drawn only from the opposite sump(s) and not cause the blockage or bather to be entrapped under suction.

The treated heated water will then pass back into the pool via inlets fitted into the pool, sited to ensure an even flow of water across the pool and then back to the sumps and skimmers. This type of swimming pool is known as a 'skimmer pool' or 'freeboard pool'.

DECK LEVEL AND INFINITY EDGE POOLS

The other type of swimming pool filtration system, which has already been mentioned with the pool finishes, is 'deck level' or 'infinity edge'.

In these instances the skimmers are substituted for a gully around the pool. This is either a deck level gully, or a channel or gully at one or more sides of the pool. These are usually set lower, to create an 'infinity edge' collection gully.

This is essentially an alternative filtration system to the skimmer pool and arguably better technically as, instead of specific locations where pool surface water is drawn off, more water is evenly filtered over the surface of the pool and, in the case of the deck level pool, 100% of the surface water can percolate over. Typically, this type of swimming pool is installed for aesthetic reasons rather than technical reasons. For both deck level swimming pools and infinity edge pools, the water overflows the pool and is collected by gravity in an underground tank or large holding tank, which is known as a balance tank.

The pool water is then drawn from the balance tank under suction from the main pool circulation pump. It is then returned to the pool, the same way as the skimmer pool, through the wall or, preferably, floor inlets.

Drawing the water away from the top of the pool, it is better in the case of deck level pools to input the pool water into the bottom and ensure an even flow of filtered water throughout the pool.

This type of installation is more complex to install than a skimmer pool. It is also more complex to run and maintain as well as more prone to running problems. For example, in a power-off situation, as water is inclined to find its own level between the pool and the balance tank, the balance tank can overflow as it is considerably smaller in volumetric capacity.

Furthermore, this type of pool is at least 25% more expensive than the traditional skimmer pool. One obvious drawback of the outdoor deck level or infinity edge swimming pool is that any leaves will collect on the surround grating or in the infinity channel. For all these reasons the domestic outdoor swimming pool is nearly always a skimmer pool.

TMD – OFF – ON

LIGHT

OFF – ON

OFF – ON

OFF – ON

REM – OFF – ON

SPA

FILTER PUMP

RUNNING   TRIPPED

BOOST PUMP

RUNNING   TRIPPED

AIR BLOWER

RUNNING   TRIPPED

BUBBLES BLOWER

RUNNING   TRIPPED

OZONE

DOSING UNIT

U/W LIGHTS

TMD – OFF – ON

REM – OFF – ON

REM – OFF – ON

REM – OFF – ON

OFF – ON

OFF – ON

REM – OFF – ON

PUMP CIRCUITS
OFF
NOT–ENERGISED

PUMP CIRCUITS
ENERGISED

RESET EMERGENCY STOP
ENERGISE
PUMP CIRCUITS

POWER
ON

MCB
TRIPPED

EMERGENCY

STOP

HIGH LIMIT STAT

29°

SPA TEMPERATURE
BOOST TEMPERATURE

9.

SPA
HEAT UP

HEAT
ON

BOOST
ON

SPA TEMPERATURE
DESIRED TEMPERATURE

9.8

240V SPA MOTORISED VALVE

OPEN

CLOSE

HIGH
LIMIT

HEAT EXCHANGER
MOTORISED VALVE

OFF – ON

PUMPS AND FILTERS

When designing the filtration system, the main design variant is the amount of time it will take the filtration and disinfection to undertake one complete cycle of treatment. This is known as the turnover rate. To put this into context, a commercial swimming pool used for lane swimming is recommended to have a two hour filtration cycle or 'two hour turnover'. These turnover rates are set by professional bodies such as SPATA, PWTAG and the Health and Safety Executive. Alternatively, private heated swimming pools are recommended at six hours, while commercial hydro spa pools are recommended at eight minutes. We work on a five to six hour turnaround rate for domestic pools. A private outdoor unheated swimming pool is recommended at no more than eight hours.

As the swimming pool designer calculates the size of the pool and the amount of water in it (the volumetric capacity) the designer can then decide what size filtration system is required for that particular pool. A large 25m x 12m swimming pool may hold something like 400m^3 of water, which is 400,000 litres. To achieve a two hour turnover, the filtration system must, therefore, be capable of circulating 200m^3 of water per hour.

This is the starting point for sizing and specifying any filtration and disinfection system. Once the designer has selected the turnover rate and knows the performance required for the filtration system, the pumps can be sized and then the filters can also be sized. The filter and pump must be selected in tandem. A too powerful pump for a small filter, for example, will cause the pool water to bore through the media or even crack or explode the filter tank; whilst a too small pump for a large filter will have no effect at all and will never backwash properly.

Once the filter and pump are sized, the final choice is how to disinfect the pool water.

FILTRATION

Using the commercial pool as an example, and getting slightly more complex, there are three defined rates that quantify the flow of the pool water across (through) the filter media. Low, medium and high.

The slower the pool water passes over the filter media, the lower the rate and better the filtration quality. Low rate filtration is generally not used for swimming pool filtration and is more widely used for portable water purification.

Since the mid 1990's it has become universally accepted that commercial pools should be filtered at a medium rate filtration, which is more effective and therefore, a more desirable filtration rate. Medium rate filtration is in the region of $20m^3/m^2/hour - 30m^3/m^2/hour$. For the 25m x 12m pool that we are using as an example (which is $400m^3$), to give a two hour turnover rate at a filtration rate of $25m^3/m^2/hour$ results in something like two 10hp pumps and two 2.5m diameter filters. Large filters like this are costly, so by installing smaller filters the savings are fairly considerable, but by keeping the pumps the same size the filtration rate will increase exponentially. A high rate is typically $30m^3/m^2/hour$ up to no more than $50m^3/m^2/hour$, beyond which point the water is being pushed through the filter so fast that the pool water does not have 'time' to be filtered effectively. In contrast, to gain a slower filtration rate, the filter becomes larger.

For a domestic swimming pool, high rate filtration is perfectly acceptable, as installing such a large filter to gain better filtration quality would generally be considered over specifying. The cost of the larger filters would be disproportionate to the task in hand and also domestic swimming pools are infinitely lower use than a commercial pool. A typical 10m x 5m swimming pool would be fitted with something like a 600mm diameter filter powered by a 1hp pump operating at high rate filtration. This system is commonly known as 'high rate sand filtration'. There will always be some individuals who require optimal filtration solutions and, therefore, on occasion medium rate filtration is fitted to domestic pools.

Filtering cleans the water by removing debris and small particles of dirt, hair, lint etc, which collects within the filter on the filter bed. The filter usually contains layers of graded sands or sometimes more specialist media, such as diatomaceous earth ('DE'), glass beads or types of volcanic rock (known by various trade names). These are designed to pick up even smaller particles such as dissolved solids. Larger items are collected in a removable strainer within the pump itself, in a chamber with an access lid.

As the smaller debris passes through the pump strainer and is collected on the filter media, pressure rises as it becomes less easy for water to pass through this layer of dirt to the media beneath. The pressure within the filter is measured by a pressure gauge which, with a clean filter bed, would circulate water at its 'normal running pressure'. As the pressure on the gauge rises, this indicates that the debris on top of the filter media is building up and the filter is in need of a backwash.

Filters are usually configured with collection nozzles or plates at the bottom of the filter vessel, which is often fibreglass. Other materials can be used such as steel with an internal lining, particularly for commercial pools. Within the filter there is a layer of media, (e.g. sand) and a distribution header spreads the pool water over the filter media. The backwash process involves repositioning flow water valves on the filter pipework, or on a more compact valve known as a multiport valve. Once the valves are repositioned, the pump pushes water in reverse through the filter, dislodging the built up dirt and debris and washing it to the drain. This backwash process is required on a regular basis, subject to the pool usage and type, but weekly or every two weeks would be recommended. Every five to ten years the media within the filter will require removing and recharging with fresh media.

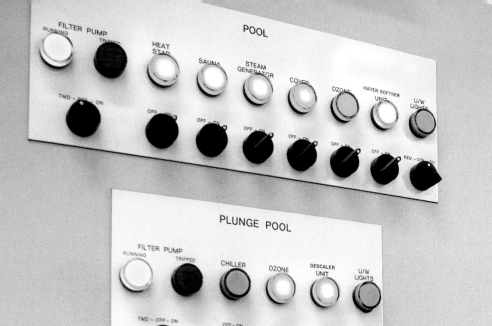

POOL

FILTER PUMP
RUNNING · TRIPPED · HEAT STAT · SAUNA · STEAM GENERATOR · COVER · OZONE · WATER SOFTNER UNIT · U/W LIGHTS

TMD - OFF - ON · OFF - ON · OFF - ON · OFF - ON · OFF - ON · OFF - ON · OFF - ON · REM - OFF - ON

PLUNGE POOL

FILTER PUMP
RUNNING · TRIPPED · CHILLER · OZONE · DESCALER UNIT · U/W LIGHTS

TMD - OFF - ON · OFF - ON · OFF - ON · OFF - ON · REM - OFF - ON

SPA

FILTER PUMP
RUNNING · TRIPPED · BOOST PUMP RUNNING · TRIPPED · AIR BLOWER RUNNING · TRIPPED · BUBBLES BLOWER RUNNING · TRIPPED · OZONE · DOSING UNIT · U/W LIGHTS

TMD - OFF - ON · REM - OFF - ON · REM - OFF - ON · REM - OFF - ON · OFF - ON · OFF - ON · REM - OFF - ON

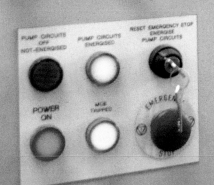

PUMP CIRCUITS OFF NOT-ENERGISED · PUMP CIRCUITS ENERGISED · RESET EMERGENCY STOP ENERGISE PUMP CIRCUITS

POWER ON · MCE TRIPPED · EMERGENCY STOP

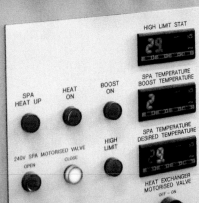

HIGH LIMIT STAT
29

SPA HEAT UP · HEAT ON · BOOST ON

SPA TEMPERATURE BOOST TEMPERATURE
2

240V SPA MOTORISED VALVE
OPEN · CLOSE · HIGH LIMIT

SPA TEMPERATURE DESIRED TEMPERATURE
29

HEAT EXCHANGER MOTORISED VALVE
OFF - ON

HEATING RETURN · HEATING FLOW · HOT WATER FLOW · HOT WATER

PRIMARY DISINFECTION

When sized and installed correctly, the filter and pump configuration will keep the pool water clean, but not disinfected. The disinfection part of the equation kills bacteria.

Domestic pools are often hand dosed with chlorine, which can be purchased off-the-shelf or via the Internet. The chlorine can be introduced directly into the pool water in granular or liquid form, or via tablets placed in the surface water skimmers. There are other disinfectants such as bromine, or more recently, hydrogen peroxide and salt water chlorination, which by means of an item of plant fitted in the plant room and connected to the pool water circulation pipe work, converts salt (suspended in solution in the pool water) into chlorine.

However, the most common disinfectant by far is chlorine. This is because, not only is it the cheapest of all the options, but it is also the more effective. As a comparison with bromine, chlorine is generally half the price, yet twice as effective.

The key to a pleasant swimming environment is not so much about the election of the disinfectant itself, but more the quantity that is introduced into the pool water.

Hand dosing any chemical into the pool water will have a very oscillating effect on chemical levels when measured. In order to benefit from definitive swimming conditions and water chemistry, an automatic chemical dosing system could be fitted. This type of equipment is very good at monitoring and adjusting the disinfectant and pH levels, but is a technical item of plant that requires a competent trained operator.

Normally, pool water naturally rises in pH (measure of the acidity / alklanity), but should remain more or less neutral at 7 or ideally the same pH as a human eye, which is 7.4. Acid solution is therefore dosed to bring the pH value back down again. This can be introduced into the pool water by hand in the form of sodium bisulphate granules which have been dissolved, or via an automatic dosing system.

The automatic dosing system comprises of a central item of plant that monitors the pool water, tests for pH and disinfectant levels and adjusts by injecting the appropriate chemical via metering pumps and small day tanks, which typically hold 100 or 200 litres of the chemical (e.g liquid chlorine, sodium hypochlorite and dry acid in solution). This system can also be used to introduce a flocculent into the pool water which gels onto small particles and minerals suspended in the pool water, allowing the pool filtration system to collect them up instead of bypassing the filter media due to size.

In rare cases, and for various reasons, the pool water can become acidic and the pH needs raising. In these instances soda ash is introduced into the pool water to raise the pH back up to 7.4.

Automatic dosing systems do give finite swimming conditions when operated correctly but are relatively expensive and quite complex to operate. Whilst they are nearly always fitted to commercial swimming pools, they are not so common on domestic swimming pools for all these reasons.

SECONDARY DISINFECTION

So far we have talked about what is known as primary disinfection, with chlorine being the most common chemical used. By installing a secondary disinfection system such UV (ultra violet) or ozone, it is possible to ease the burden on the primary disinfectant and allow less chemical use. This is very desirable as not only are there significant cost savings (particularly for the commercial pool), but also the swimming environment is greatly enhanced.

In layman's terms, UV disinfection (pool water washes over an ultra violet lamp) and ozone disinfection (electrically generated O_3 gas is bubbled into the water and then removed by a de-gassing system as it is toxic to humans), will kill bacteria in the pool water. Both these systems are specialist items of pool plant and are fitted in the plant room. They will work generating either UV or ozone all the time the filtration plant is on. The more powerful the kit (and of course the more expensive) the more bacteria will be killed and the less chlorine will be used. To put this into context, a typical swimming pool would be run at around 1.5ppm (parts per million) to 2.0ppm chlorine, but with a reasonable UV or ozone system this could be lowered to around 1.0ppm (it does vary on how much sunlight and use the pool gets). Drinking water can fluctuate in chlorine levels up to 1.0ppm but is normally in the 0.3 – 0.5ppm range.

By adding a good quality UV or ozone plant into the filtration set up, chemical usage and levels are halved. It is never possible to completely eliminate the need for a primary disinfectant and the rule of thumb is that the better quality or higher dosage the UV or ozone system fitted, the lower the chlorine levels can be. It is possible to get chlorine levels down to incoming tap water level using a 'full ozone system', which gives the pool water a very high dosage of ozone compared to domestic systems. This is reserved for commercial pools or very high specification domestic pools where cost is no issue, as these systems are tens of thousands of pounds.

chapter 4

'HEATING, COVERS, LIGHTING & TECHNOLOGY'

How to heat indoor and outdoor swimming pools, options on pool covers and how this impacts pool heating. Underwater lighting and how new technologies impact all of these aspects of a successful swimming pool project.

POOL HEATING

The principals of heating an outdoor swimming pool and an indoor swimming pool are very different.

OUTDOOR SWIMMING POOLS

An outdoor swimming pool is filtered, as previously described, and then the pool water is passed by a heater to heat the pool water to typically 28°C - 30°C (80°F).

The type of heater will depend on the source and cost of energy available at the property, so it may be a gas boiler, oil boiler, propane boiler, heat exchanger connected to existing boilers or even an electrical heater. This often depends on the views of the customer.

There is solar, and also air source heating, which features a unit using electricity to convert latent heat in the atmosphere for heat input into the pool water. This offers the advantage that anything up to 4kW of heat can be created using only 1kW of electricity. The technical measure for this performance is the COP (Coefficient of Production) - in this case 4:1 - which varies according to the warmth of the atmosphere.

Alternatively, ground source heating is similar to air source but takes heat from coils or deep bore holes in the earth where the soil is a static temperature and, therefore, has latent heat available.

These 'green' energy sources have become much more popular and mainstream in the last decade. However, in the colder, less sunny parts of the world, it may be advisable for a traditional heater (e.g gas boiler) to be fitted as a back up heating system to bring the pool up to temperature in the first instance of filling the pool, after refilling, after winter shut down or when the green energy source is not performing so well. The boiler can be set so that the green energy source is prioritised and the back up boiler only kicks in when needed. In countries where summers are not always guaranteed to be hot, outdoor swimming pools with green energy heating systems would definitely benefit from a back up boiler to ensure the pool is usable throughout these months.

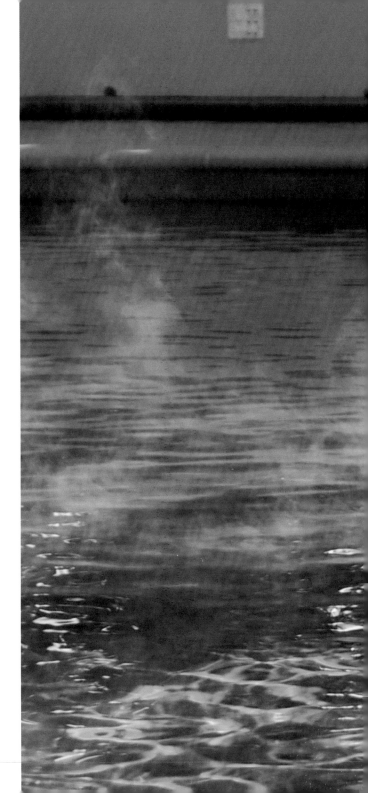

INDOOR SWIMMING POOLS

Indoor swimming pools are heated in an entirely different way, using a different system. All swimming pools lose the majority of heat through the surface water due to convection and evaporation, which can be controlled to a large degree, by deploying a pool cover. With an indoor pool, the evaporation will manifest itself as condensation on the coldest parts of the building, normally the window glazing. However, as glazing manufacturers have improved the U value (measure of insulation) of glazing through gas filled, double and triple glazed units, more often these days it is the window frame that attracts condensation. This condensation is highly damaging to any building fabric as it can contain hypochlorous acid and, therefore, condensation must be controlled in the indoor pool.

The indoor pool water (as per the outdoor pool) is usually heated to around 28°C and, by heating the pool hall air to 1°C hotter than the pool water at ALL times, the pool water will not want to evaporate and condensation will be kept under control. It is therefore the pool air that requires heating more than the pool water for an indoor pool. Excluding the initial heat up of the pool water, the energy used for topping up the pool water heat is about 10% of the total energy required for the heating to the pool hall air.

The most desirable method of heating the pool air is to utilise a central air handling plant specifically made for indoor swimming pools. The air handling unit is capable of heating the pool hall air, using heating coils and fans to deliver the heated air via under-floor or overhead (concealed or sometimes on show, in the overhead case) ducting and grille apertures, taking it onto the coldest parts of the building (usually the glazing or window frames). By 'air washing' the coldest parts of the building in this manner, the condensation is kept at bay. Of course, it is not possible to air wash every square millimetre of the building and on colder days condensation will still occur; it is all about mitigating the extent of the condensation.

The central air handling unit will dehumidify (keeping humidity levels in the pool hall to 60%RH), heat the pool water itself and also has the ability to exhaust stale air from the atmosphere and bring in fresh air. The pool hall air is returned to the air handling unit via a pool hall grille and circulated through the unit, heated and then returned to the pool hall by the under floor or overhead ducting. The air handling unit requires electricity to run and also needs primary hot water connections to a dedicated boiler or the boiler system for the house / building, which may well provide heat to radiators or cylinders as well.

As described previously, the desire for a 'green energy' system has become much more popular and it is of no real consequence how the primary hot water is provided (i.e. whether it is a biomass boiler, air source, ground source etc), although the primary water should ideally be delivered at 80°C. In cases where this is not possible (ground source systems generally provide their primary heat at a much lower 45-55°C), a larger than normal heat exchanger has to be pre-fitted within the air handling unit to compensate and 'to absorb' more of the heat from the lower temperature primary hot water.

As one can appreciate, the system described is quite complex and therefore costly to install. Consequently, there are alternative solutions available to heat the pool air. One such solution is to install a smaller style air handling unit that is pushed up to a dividing wall between the pool hall and another room (nearly always the pool plant room). This sucks the wet air through a lower wall louvre and blows heated dry air through a higher louvre. The obvious downside is the air washing process does not occur without the ducting. However, the installation cost is significantly less than the ducted solution – around half the cost. Another option is to use wall mounted dehumidifiers with heating batteries, coupled with Indux fans for stale air exhaust. Again, this will not air wash the glazing but it is a less costly solution.

In situations when the indoor pool is covered with a manual or automatic pool cover or with a moving floor system, then the pool water, as previously mentioned, is less able to condensate. In these instances the air handling unit can be pre-programmed to drop the air temperature back to a cooler temperature, such as 24°C, which of course saves energy.

Contrary to the common assumption that covering the pool water saves heat and therefore reduces the heating of the pool water, it in fact saves heating the air. For a domestic indoor pool where the pool may only be used for short periods of time, say an hour a day, having a pool cover to cover the pool water for the other twenty three hours a day is quite desirable in terms of energy saving.

With the advent of automated pool covers and motors compatible with swimming pool usage, a lot of the 'issues' associated with manual pool covers are overcome, namely ease of use all year round, heat retention and safety.

POOL COVERS, MOVING FLOORS & WALLS

The advent of mechanical moving parts and motors working in harmony with swimming pools and swimming pool water has, since the 1990's, allowed innovative companies and creative individuals to invent new technology for swimming pools, offering previously unavailable levels of safety, heat retention and usability.

In most countries it would be inconceivable to install an outdoor swimming pool, as well as a large proportion of indoor swimming pools, without a pool cover.

FLOATING POOL COVERS

Heat retention floating pool covers have been available for swimming pools since the 1960's and there are two types. The floating bubble cover (typically blue in colour) has a reel system that straps to the cover and is manually rolled out of the pool and onto the reel. These covers need protection from the sun and must be covered by a solar protector sheet when rolled up. The reel system can be bolted to the floor or can be fitted with castors which allow the user to manoeuvre the cover and reel system away from the pool if needed. The cover can also be folded as it is rolled in, which means in can be used on shaped pools. This type of cover is actually relatively inexpensive and very good at retaining heat. It will probably pay for itself in terms of energy costs saved over two or three years which, when compared to other systems, is very impressive.

The obvious downside to a floating pool cover is that it is not particularly quick or easy to remove and replace, and on larger pools this would be a two person job. Also the reel and cover are not pleasing to the eye. There is also the issue of safety – an animal or human traversing onto this cover would become engulfed and could potentially drown. There is an argument that this type of cover on a pool is more dangerous than the pool being left uncovered. Finally the lifespan of this type of cover is really only three or four years – they degrade due to the elements (sun and wind) and wear, through general usage.

A similar system to that described above is the floating thermal cover, which can be described as floating, compressed foam. Again, typically a blue colour, the compressed foam material also floats on the pool surface. These are more robust and thicker than the bubble cover, more expensive and much more unwieldy to handle. More than one reel system could be required if used on larger pools (or even moderate sized pools) and consequently they are mostly used on small spas and hydrotherapy pools. Like the bubble cover, this system is very good at heat retention, but again its lifespan is quite short as they have a tendency to become water logged.

For the outdoor pool during the winter months, it would be routine to pack away the manual heat retention cover and deploy the winter debris cover. These green 'Courweave' covers are pinned down into the surround paving and left over the 'winterised' pool throughout the winter months. These have the advantage of sealing off the pool from leaves and debris. However, it is not uncommon to remove the debris cover in spring to find a green pool.

AUTOMATED POOL COVERS

There are two types of automated pool cover and within those two genres, many alternative manufacturers and styles – all with their own pros and cons.

SLATTED POOL COVERS

The slatted pool cover could be briefly described as a venetian blind that rolls out onto the pool surface from a concealed pit. The system is powered by a small low voltage motor in an adjacent 'motor pit' or more commonly (in more recent years) from a rotating motor inside the reel (spindle) beneath the pool water and inside the pool cover pit.

The slats are made from PVC and can be customised to almost any colour (white or neutral colours are most commonly used), or can even be transparent, which looks quite impressive and can be mostly seen on indoor pools. On outdoor pools it is common to see the solar gain enhancing slat, which is transparent with a black backing to trap the heat from the sun. The solar gain enhancing slats work very well and on a winter's day with the sun out, this is very noticeable in the top 100mm of pool water under the pool cover, which will be warm.

The slats measure approximately 50mm – 65mm each and interlink to form a properly clipped together cover. Once clipped together, the design is such that it requires a skilled engineer to unclip them for removal / replacement. It is relatively uncommon, therefore, for the slats to separate whilst in use. Each slat has three compartments, two of which are filled with air, thus making the cover buoyant. This type of cover is excellent at heat retention and solar gain (if a solar gain slat is fitted). Due to the buoyancy of the pool cover this will support a human being or animal – although it is not considered advisable or recommended to walk on them.

Safety can be enhanced by supporting the cover at the edges of the pool by a handrail or support ledge just under the pool water level. In France it is stipulated via the 'norme française' for this type of cover to comply to the requirement for a pool to satisfy certain safety standards – that this type of pool cover must be able to support a man's weight plus 50kg (about 140kg). It also stipulates that the cover must be clipped in at the far end to avoid it being lifted and to prevent people or animals getting under the cover and becoming trapped. It would be worth expanding on the French safety standards to say that pools must feature a compliant safety feature against drowning – comprising either, or a combination of the following – pool cover, fencing or alarm around the pool, or alarm in the pool water.

The slatted pool cover can be housed in a floor or wall pit with tiled panels supported by a stainless steel frame. These usually have a 50mm slot across the wall or floor of the pool to let the cover pass out, or on more high-tech installations, it is possible to have the stainless steel frame motorised – which lifts before the pool cover is deployed - the advantage being, there is no slot. The more traditional way to house the pool cover is at one end of the pool (most commonly the deep end so the housing does not interfere with pool user traffic) under a support beam with decking or paving spanning the pool. This type of pit is constructed adjacent to the pool, underground and flooded with pool water. The mouth or opening to the 'letterbox' or 'traditional pit' must correspond to the skimmer mouths that govern the water level e.g. the pool cover floats out on the water level from the centre of the opening to the traditional pit.

The downside of the traditional pit is that often the support beam has to be quite robust to support the whole span of the pool and its surround paving (robust meaning a sizeable beam). If one requires the surround to be flush, this will impact water level and skimmer position, resulting in quite a large freeboard (distance from surround edge tile or coping to water level) to accommodate the beam. This can be circumnavigated by accepting a raised decking to the far end of the pool, which we will explore in the chapters to come, as adding three dimensions to a pool scheme in this way can bring the design together. Whether the housing is the traditional method or wall or floor, the size of the housing is quite large – on average 800mm x 800mm clear space, or even bigger for large pools. Sometimes the pool cover is housed in an above ground wooden or powder coated aluminium box, but this is quite rare (and unsightly) and really reserved for the retro fit solution.

Clearly, all pool covers are suited to rectangular pools, but with clever location of the pool cover pit, or indeed a central floor pit with two cover systems passing up onto the pool surface in two directions, it is possible to cover shaped pools with slatted pool covers. The more complex the installation, the more the system will cost to install.

In summary, slatted pool covers are very good at heat retention and solar gain. Concealed well, so aesthetically they work well, they give ease of use and access to the pool and it is feasible to use the outdoor pool well into the extended season or indeed all year round. They add a dimension of enhanced safety to the pool but, in my opinion, a pool cover should not be fitted to a scheme for this reason as even with a pool cover – swimming pools should always be considered a potential hazard.

Finally, the cost of this type of cover solution is not inexpensive and this should be borne in mind. Although, as previously mentioned, it is almost inconceivable to install a luxury pool in modern times without an automatic pool cover, it is unlikely to ever pay for itself in terms of energy savings. The life span for this type of pool cover is ten to fifteen years and the starting price is circa £15,000.

STRETCH OVER COVERS

The other type of automated pool cover is the stretch over type. These are a bit more limited in terms of location of pool cover pit and shape of pool. The PVC material is pulled across the top of the pool on aluminium runners fitted under the pool coping or sometimes (usually on retro fit) behind the pool coping in the pool surround. This system is really only suited to rectangular pools. A shaped or Roman end opposite the pool cover pit end can only be accommodated by the surface runner option, which will extend beyond the shaped end, pulling the cover over that area of pool zone as well. On the plus side, the cover pit housing is relatively small compared to the needs (and rolled up size) of the slatted pool cover – and is usually about 450mm x 450mm, which in turn makes concealing or covering the pit with decking or paving a lot less challenging.

The aluminium runners are always sited at each length of the pool and incorporate pulleys and steel reinforced pull cords which, when the motor (low voltage or hydraulic with the power pack sited remotely - i.e. in the plant room) is activated, it drags the cover out or back into the cover pit. The visible part of the runner is about 50mm in size.

Once this type of pool cover is on the pool it is very safe in terms of people or animals being able to penetrate through it as it is locked into the runners, adding to its reputation of being the safest type of pool cover. However, as per my previous statement, even pools with this type of pool cover can still be hazardous. For example, when fitted to an outdoor pool, the cover will harbour rainfall and, although small pumps are supplied / recommended to lay on the pool cover to deal with this, they can block, not be turned on, or fail, in which case this creates a slippery pool of water up to 300mm deep.

In summary, this type of pool cover is the safest, but is not as good at heat retention or solar gain. It is not so versatile in terms of shape and it is not pretty due to the aluminium runners located in a visually critical location in terms of design.

Both stretch over and slatted pool covers are operated by a keyswitch and cannot be activated without the key. They also incorporate an emergency stop button. The keyswitch must be positioned within full line of sight of the swimming pool to prevent the pool cover being operated whilst in use. The keyswitch can be supplemented by a touch pad or as part of the house management system, as long as the features are as described above.

As an alternative method of heat retention, liquid pool covers exist. These comprise of small dosing systems that inject a non toxic chemical compound, which lays unseen on the pool water surface to prevent or slow down heat loss through the surface of the pool water.

MOVING FLOORS

For the ultimate 'cover' solution we have moving floors. Through research and development into motors for pool covers, hydraulic and electrical motors have been used to power moving floor structures strong enough to support a finished (tiled) floor. Whilst moving floors have been used for many years in the commercial swimming pool sector, these tended to be rigid plastic with runners (or worm drives) set in the pool wall. For a commercial pool the most important thing is versatility; a moving floor allows a diving pool to be turned into a learner pool at the touch of button – no matter what it looks like.

For the more discerning private client who requires a luxury pool, it would not be in keeping with high end finishes to incorporate a 'plastic' moving floor with visible runners in the pool wall. By forming an unusually deep swimming pool structure, water based hydraulic rams can be concealed under a stainless steel structure with buoyancy packs, which can be tiled to match the pool finishes or pool hall surround finishes. Only two tiled removable 'man ways' are set into the moving floor (600mm x 600mm) for access into the void below. Clearly this is very desirable and has become available as an option due to the advent of new technologies.

A moving floor is the ultimate in terms of safety, heat retention and appearance and can obviously double up as an internal space, dance hall, function room or patio area for an external pool. There are shape limitations for moving floor pools as they are suited to rectangular pools, but can be more tailored. For instance, one of Guncast's recent designs includes a step bay adjacent to the main pool body with two sets of cantilever steps, so anything is possible!

The theory behind this type of moving floor is that it floats, due to the buoyancy packs. Stainless steel cables attached to the ram, 'pull' the floor down (it can be stopped at any level to the bottom of its travel) and holds the floor down when the pool is being used for swimming. In the up position the floor floats but also locks into the pool wall via a number of automated locking pins which locate into recessed apertures in the pool wall. (Typically, six holes of around 63mm diameter sleeved with stainless steel – relatively discrete). Before water-based hydraulics, external motors were used. They connected to the floor via a very large conduit from the motor in the plant room to the pool (the conduit would be as large as 300mm diameter). This system, in principal, achieves the same, but is a bit more cumbersome.

It goes without saying that the moving floor pool is very expensive and in a price bracket all of its own. With the additional structural work, the additional demands on the air handling system (which is desirable to be able to cool as well for function room use), additional water to filter and the pool floor itself – a budget of £500,000 is realistic.

MOVING WALLS

Moving walls or 'booms' were initially used in commercial pools to automatically divide pools in half (or any increment) to create a zone for serious swimmers and a child's zone, for example. Using the same technology as for moving floors, moving walls have been incorporated into domestic pools, which span from indoors to outdoors and can divide off the outdoor pool when not in use. Coupled with a slatted pool cover on the outdoor section of pool and a moving floor on the indoor pool – the ultimate in swimming pools can be built!

Whether we are discussing pool covers or moving floors, it is clear that a rectangular pool is the most compatible shape. This has really led away from the curved and kidney shaped pools of the 1980's and nearly all pools built in the UK in modern times are rectangular for this reason. In America there is still a plethora of shaped pools being built but I suspect that, as the USA becomes more environmentally aware, there will be a trend towards rectangular pools there in the future.

UNDERWATER LIGHTING

Traditional underwater pool lighting consists of floodlights, usually sited shining away from swimming lanes and away from sitting areas around the pool.

These types of underwater lights are relatively powerful, (a 300W flood lamp is the norm) and are about 300mm in diameter. Two lights would quite adequately illuminate an 11m x 5m pool. The source of light, if sited as above, is ideally not seen and the light will illuminate the pool water, giving a fairly even glow all over the pool. From a distance, an outdoor pool at night, lit as above, will look warm and inviting.

In recent years the trend has been toward fitting smaller, less powerful lights in larger quantities. This gives a completely different type of light effect because beams of light are omitted from the light source across the pool water. Using the same sized pool as an example (11m x 5m), installing 50 watt lights (either halogen bulbs or LED light sources), which are about 70mm in diameter, one could site eight lights down one length of the pool, or six down each length.

Whether the lights are small or large, they are typically built into the pool wall in niche housing at around 300mm - 450mm below the water level. They are subsequently connected to the plant room and transformer (the bulbs have to be low voltage e.g. 12V) via steel wire armoured cable and a pool surround electrical connection box or 'deck box'. The depth of the light niche is predominately quite high in the pool water because, as a part of a maintenance regime, the light bulb may need removing from its housing and floating to the surface so that the necessary maintenance to the 'light guts' can be undertaken at pool side. If the light is deeper into the pool water, it becomes a much more complicated operation to unscrew the light and let it float up and, in general, the depth of the light has little impact on how the pool water illuminates, unless the pool is unusually deep. There are lighting schemes for swimming pools which have larger numbers of lights and on the pool floor – but these are always fibre optic or LED schemes.

Fibre optic lighting schemes are very well suited to swimming pools as the light source is usually in the plant room, meaning if a bulb needs changing this is very easy. One 250W light source is capable of feeding light through (glass or PMMA) fifteen multi strand fibre optic cables. These terminate in niche housings, embedded in the pool with stainless steel bezels (70mm diameter) and different shaped lenses, which contort the light at a wide angle or direct a pin point of light (useful for setting into the sides of pool steps to highlight the edge of the treads). There is a maximum run or cable length of about 12m -15m at which point the light strength starts to weaken, but this can be circumnavigated by adding further light sources into the scheme.

It is not uncommon to use two or three light sources to achieve the desired effect, particularly as the light output is much weaker than traditional bulbs, and for an 11m x 5m pool, at least 15 light emitters would be required, possibly even thirty. The light sources often include a colour wheel which, when activated, rotates in front of the bulb, which in turn changes the hue of light in the pool water.

Whilst fibre optic and LED underwater lighting schemes are versatile and can be used to produce all sorts of effects and colours, they are in a completely different price bracket when compared to the traditional underwater pool flood light.

Other variants of the fibre optic pool lighting solution are fibre optic strips, which we normally set just under an overhanging pool coping, or pin points set into the pool floor, which give a twinkle or 'star light' effect. These pin points are fitted the same way as the multistrand housings but are much smaller, such as 20mm stainless steel square niches, holding two or three strands. Again, the more hi-tech and complex the scheme, the more expensive it becomes. We have installed some fibre optic schemes for swimming pools, which have cost in excess of £100,000.

LED swimming pool lighting is very similar to the fibre optic scheme in terms of the end result. 70mm pool wall niches are available, as are lighting strips and smaller and larger units depending on what is trying to be achieved.

The main advantage of LED pool lighting is that, in essence, a printed circuit board and light emitter connected to a controller, can be programmed to do almost anything in terms of colour or speeds of flashing. This might be useful if the pool owner requires the pool to be a specific colour at any given time with 'mood settings'. For example, red for invigoration and warmth or blue for cool and calming. Alternatively, the pool owner may want to use a line of LED lights in the pool floor as a timer to swim up against.

The LED works off individual printed circuit boards in each light fitted, which gives it all its advantages but this can also be a disadvantage. In general LED lights have thousands of hours use before they require replacing. However, if water does manage to penetrate the waterproof sealant the printed circuit board is encased in, it will fail. When continuously submerged in swimming pool water the LED light is obviously more susceptible to water penetration, compared to when sited in dry areas. Although very good quality LED underwater pool lights are less prone to this problem, LED lights can fail for this reason. To remedy a failed LED is not a case of switching a component or part – the whole unit has to be replaced, making it quite expensive if this occurs. A good quality underwater LED light unit is circa £300.

Over the last ten years in London (as in other densely populated cities around the world), space has become more and more premium and desirable.

Extending properties in the normal way (upward or outward) has become impossible due to congestion of adjoining properties. Therefore to circumnavigate this problem the trend has been to extend downwards by underpinning and forming a basement under exclusive properties, thereby adding extra square feet of valuable space.

These spaces can then be 'fitted out' to accommodate swimming pools and other facilities. Due to space restraints in cities, in some instances (particularly with commercial pools) it is not unheard of to 'have' to build swimming pools on first floors, which creates its own set of problems as to what happens to the leakage and spillage. As previously mentioned, it is generally accepted that all pools are likely to leak to a very minor degree.

Using London as an example, a typical scenario would be that specialist basement contractors have been underpinning, excavating, and forming huge watertight basements under existing properties. In some cases these basements are multi level, or two or three storey. Once the basement is built, the area can be fitted out according to the client's desires.

To undertake this type of project is a major commitment both financially and in terms of time. To reach the point where the basement can be fitted out would probably take a year of planning and a further year on site. The technicalities and logistical issues involved in working in built up cities, make the process lengthy. Whilst less demanding, the fitting out of the basement could take another year. If the client is incorporating a swimming pool into the basement, I would suggest the starting budget should be £1,000,000; and of course the sky is the limit.

Project 'Mayfair' is a town villa in Mayfair, London. This particular client required additional space to accommodate garaging, some relaxing space, a gym and a swimming pool. The only option was to excavate downward and form a basement with mechanical lifting for the cars and to accommodate all of the above.

PROJECT 'MAYFAIR'

Although the basement zone was the same size as the footprint of the existing house, there was much to be fitted in there and so the basement was formed with unusually high ceilings. It should be recognised every 100mm extra of formation will result in additional thousands to the cost. This particular client realised that forming the basement with 2.7m high ceilings would add a level of unrivalled luxury to the project.

Whilst generally the basement was formed to this depth, about one third of the basement was formed a further 2m deeper, thus creating a zone for swimming pool construction, a service crawl way around the pool structure and a two tier plant room.

The principal behind this method of construction (which is often adopted for basement swimming pool construction) is that the 'outer' basement or box structure – having little or (ideally) no penetrations through it (unlike a swimming pool) - can be formed watertight. The lowest point of the basement is then fitted with a pumped chamber to pump away any water that gets into the basement or escapes from the pool through spillage etc. The swimming pool structure is then formed against a permanent high grade extruded polystyrene back shutter, typically termed the 'inner box'.

Careful planning and design allows a service zone around the pool for air ducting into the pool hall and pool circulation pipework, and often some of the plant, or all of the plant, itself. This was the case for project 'Mayfair', although due to space constraints some of the plant, pumps and filters were located in the service void and accessed through a hatch in the upper plant room floor, where the air handling unit was housed.

PROJECT 'MAYFAIR'

Although this town villa represents about 10,000ft² of living space, the newly formed basement was only 1500ft². The client who is extremely discerning in terms of taste also required a huge amount of facility built into the basement.

The pool itself needed to include a seated spa area with hydro massage jets, a vitality area with neck massage stations, a pool cover for maintaining temperatures (a vitality pool and spa area really needs the pool to run at 34°C minimum). Because the pool was relatively small – 6m x 4m, a counter current swimjet was included in order to allow exercise against a powerful flow of water for the swimmer to swim against. This specification coupled with the aesthetic demands of the client and his designers, resulted in a very high specification swimming pool in an extremely clean cut modern design setting.

PROJECT 'MAYFAIR'

As well as excavating and forming other tiers of basement lower into the ground, another solution (if the property has a garden) is to excavate the whole garden away and construct the basement to be under the house and under the garden, reinstating the lawn and foliage above the basement, once built.

This has the obvious advantage that the pool itself can be much bigger and also the basement can be built with rooflights, making the pool hall environment less oppressive and more airy.

In recent years there has been a definite trend toward longer pools, which allow the swimmer to train properly without the aid of swimjets.

Project 'Knightsbridge' was a former girls' school. The building was redeveloped to form a luxury 20,000ft^2 private dwelling in central London. At the time this was one of the most expensive houses in London.

Part of the project included excavating under the house itself and the entire rear garden. Concrete piles were formed around the whole garden to allow it to be safely excavated and a vast waterproof concrete basement constructed.

The basement was subsequently fitted out with a swimming pool, plant rooms, gym and a tunnel to the rear of the garden leading to garaging. The whole of the basement was sealed in with a watertight roof, on which the garden was then replanted. A section of the roof was glazed and automated to slide on and off at the touch of a button.
`
Our brief was to construct the very large pool (overall 15m x 15m), hydro spa pool (again very large at 4m x 2m), and waterfall arrangement. The pool and spa structure were built using the gunite method of concrete construction and sat within one corner of the preformed basement structure. It was then lined with waterproof render and tiled with white blend Italian glass mosaic (white tiles make the water look very blue – as you can see in the photos the pool tiles almost look blue but are, in fact, white). The surround to this pool is a mixture of Belgian granite (textured for anti-slip) and black marble. An indoor pool of this size in central London could only be achieved by the architect going to the extreme measure of excavating the whole garden. The whole project took about three years.

PROJECT 'KNIGHTSBRIDGE'

Project 'Highbury' was also a complete garden excavation, utilising the same construction sequence as project 'Knightsbridge', piling the garden to allow the vast hole to be dug. This project was constructed some years after project 'Knightsbridge', and the developer was prudent enough to build ground source heat pump coils into the concrete piles, which extract the latent heat from the surrounding earth. This in turn provides heating not only for the pool, but for the whole house.

Both these swimming pools include a spa pool which, in normal running mode, gently overflows into the main pool and shares the same heating, filtration and water disinfection plant (in both cases ozone with an automatic chemical adjustment system). In normal running mode (common mode) the spa is the same temperature as the pool. To use the spa, it must be activated into dedicated mode by way of a switch in the pool hall (or elsewhere), which then isolates the spa from the pool via automatic valves and the whole filtration and heating plant is dedicated to the spa pool.

This will heat the spa up to a higher set point (say 38°C) over half an hour or so. During this period of time the pool water is not filtered, which is perfectly acceptable for sanitisation (but if the pool is deck level or infinity edge, consideration must be taken in order to maintain the correct pool water level if swimmers are displacing pool water into a balance tank).

PROJECT 'HIGHBURY'

The advantage of the one plant system, which caters for both spa and pool, is running costs are halved (one plant in lieu of two) and capital cost in the first instance – particularly if ozone plants and automated dosing is fitted. The disadvantage is that there is a time lag waiting for the spa to heat up, which may be acceptable for domestic usage but this type of set up would never be used for commercial pools.

Project 'Highbury' was 15m long by about 3m wide and incorporated an automatic pool cover (linked to an environmental control system so that the air can be cooler than the typical pool hall temperature of 30°C when the pool cover is on the pool), concealed in the floor of the pool at the shallow end. The length of pool, ground source heating system and pool cover are much more in keeping with modern pool specifications when compared to project 'Knightsbridge'.

Really, the pool length and the heating system could only have been achieved by thinking carefully about how to develop or turn this relatively small London space into a larger one.

PROJECT 'HIGHBURY'

Another example of exceptional planning was project 'Zetland'. Working along side Milk Architecture & Design Ltd, Guncast developed the design and constructed this stunning lower basement complex, which included a swimming pool, spa, sauna, steam room and gym.

The basement was constructed in the aforementioned way, by building an outer waterproof concrete structure with a lowered zone for the swimming pool and plant room. In this instance, although the basement did extend into the rear garden, the garden was relatively small and therefore the basement could only extend back a few metres, meaning the newly formed basement was compact. Again, the brief was to incorporate lots of facilities for the clients and all these features were cleverly woven into the scheme by the design team.

PROJECT 'ZETLAND'

Another element of the brief from the client and the architect was to incorporate Italian porcelain tiles, not only in the pool and spa, but throughout the whole pool hall area, including walls and floor, with the grout lines running through and to include specially formed edge copings from the same material.

Specialist bespoke tile supplier Garth Marnoch of Stonegres was employed and comments on the project as follows:

"A technically challenging project in which the brief for us was purely stated as 'Sophisticated, stunning, clean, inviting'. The choice of materials was integral to the final expectations, although the fear of the space becoming cold and uninviting had to be dispelled from our minds. The process of achieving the desired result allowed Stonegres to be creative, whilst at all times respecting the technical issues required for a project as complex as Zetland. From the edge details, internal pool finishes, through to the customised random length mosaic, this project was definitely fulfilling and the whole team was a pleasure to work with throughout. I feel the images speak for themselves."

PROJECT 'ZETLAND'

Whilst planning an indoor pool, it may not be the small space of city living that is the issue. Project 'Thame' was a prime example of another type of space restriction. Whilst this property was a country estate with several hundred acres, the proposed indoor swimming pool was designed to replace a redundant outdoor swimming pool in a walled garden.

Planning restrictions and the garden wall itself clearly prevented a large or even ordinary sized swimming pool building from being constructed. The client and her family (who were very keen on twice daily hydrotherapeutic exercise) accepted that the indoor swimming pool that was needed to provide this facility would be small. This did not mean, however, that it would not be functional and architecturally beautiful.

The building itself was stainless steel framed with glazed walls and a central hip glazed rooflight. The pool was 4m x 4m x 1.2m deep, and fitted with two extremely powerful 'Fastlane' counter current units, each capable of pumping 5000 gallons per minute toward the swimmer. With these units fitted, two swimmers can easily exercise side by side throughout the year.

The pool and surround was clad in Italian porcelain with the grout lines following through to form the surround tiling in and back out of the pool. Ozone disinfection was fitted in tandem with the filtration system. As the pool has no pool cover, this is particularly important because the ozone breaks down the chloramines (which generate the smell associated with pool halls) and generally less chlorine is needed. This makes for a much more pleasant swimming environment – again, important when training vigorously.

The plant and air handling unit (Calorex Delta 4) were fitted in an adjacent plant room. This is quite a high capacity unit for such a small pool and pool hall, but was required to cope with the amount of glazing and the lack of a pool cover.

The return air grille is visible in the three dimensional porcelain feature wall, which has the plant room behind.

The conundrum of building pools into tight spaces does not just apply to indoor swimming pools.

Often, clients will want an outdoor swimming pool over and above an indoor swimming pool. There is also a trend toward very long thin swimming pools to allow proper swim training. Not everyone has a few million pounds spare to start excavating their garden and underpinning their house.

Although the outdoor swimming pool is not confined to walls of the property, it is confined to garden boundaries and walls.

Access into the back garden is often not easy for large excavators, as the house is usually in the way!

Project 'Richmond' classically falls into the 'small spaces' scenario. The clients (husband and wife), are very devoted and disciplined swimmers and, having an eye for design, required the privacy of being able to seriously swim at home.

The large property in leafy Richmond did not have the confines of central London but the clients' brief included a 22m long swimming pool, with a large spa at one end and a water feature at the other. The overall length was actually longer than the garden itself.

The client appointed Guncast to construct the pool, spa plant room and water features and a clever team of architects, Thompson + Baroni Architects were appointed to help with the task of fitting the pool into the garden. The architects proposed that the pool and spa would be long (as per the clients' brief) but only 3m wide, which allowed the pool to effectively run the length of the garden but also up and adjacent to the side of the house.

PROJECT 'RICHMOND'

As the pool itself took up nearly one third of the garden, no more space could be sacrificed for a plant room, especially as this specification of pool and spa needed a space of about 5m x 3m to accommodate all the plant needed.

To save space the plant room was constructed under the garden using the same methods of construction as the pool (sprayed gunite concrete and waterproof render). This housed not just the filtration, ozone and automatic disinfection plant (the spa runs on a shared filtration system) but also the feature pumps for the spa jets and lighting system. The pool and spa were built with eleven high quality stainless steel dimmable LED lights and the waterfall incorporates into the mirror polish spout, colour change fibre optics to blend colours into the water as it exits the spout.

PROJECT 'RICHMOND'

It is essential that an underground plant room is dry and includes a drain chamber with submersible pump(s) to pump any excess water or cope with a flood (for example from leaving a pump lid off). Often, two pumps are fitted as a fail-safe, but the plant will also generate heat and therefore mechanical ventilation is required to circulate the air and stop the plant room overheating. This is most important as the plant room will not continually heat up, and never flood.

Sensible and safe access into a plant room is also a prerequisite – a step ladder is not safe for carrying chemicals up and down. The plant room at project 'Richmond' was fitted with stainless steel stairs, with a handrail for safety.

The pool is finished in blue blend Italian glass mosaic, Italian grey limestone copings and surround and the waterfall is clad in Italian marble (one piece, so no jointing).

Logistically, constructing the swimming pool was quite problematic. Access to the rear of the property was via the side of the house because space at the front of the house was fairly limited. Once in the garden, the pool excavation unearthed a very robust disused basement that needed breaking out without damage to the adjacent kitchen glazing and garden wall.

This project was particularly demanding in terms of logistics, but also the clients required a very high specification large swimming pool in a relatively small garden.

PROJECT 'RICHMOND'

Ray Thompson, from Thompson + Baroni, the architect for project 'Richmond' comments:

"The notable aspect of the client's brief from the outset was that we were going to build a pool that would be used. It was definitely not going to be an ornamental feature in the garden. It should, however, still look great and tie in well with the modern cantilevered glass family room and leave enough lawn space for the family to play outdoor games.

The realisation and success of the pool and garden is entirely down to the determination of the client to achieve something beyond the ordinary that enhances the views from inside and outside the house and also serves as an incredibly versatile way to maintain healthy lives and also is a source of great fun for the family and visiting friends.

We laid out the pool in the garden so that it had a substantial length for a domestic pool- at 22m. In order to maximise the usable area of the garden all of the mechanical equipment was located in a subterranean plant room.

We looked at many finishes in and around the pool that would give the effect that we wanted and spent a lot of time deliberating over whether or not to line the pool with a cool grey stone to continue the finishes from the house to the outside. The decision to go with the random mixed blue mosaics was to ensure that even in the grey autumn days the pool still bounces light around and recalls sunnier climes.

As the pool is used many times on a daily basis it is important that the water is maintained at a useable temperature. The motorised insulated retractable cover ensures that water is always ready for use and within a few minutes the cover is opened and the pool is ready. The spa has a quick heat-up facility to bring the temperature up to the higher levels required for lounging in the bubbling water.

The focus of the pool is the Italian marble slab at the far end with a bespoke polished stainless steel, horizontal water cascade, illuminated internally with a colour change light feature."

PROJECT 'RICHMOND'

Project 'Hampstead' included an infinity edge swimming pool, finished throughout in Italian glass mosaic. The pool itself was sited adjacent to the boundary wall, which was subsequently clad in top quality Swiss granite.

As this pool was infinity edge with a pool cover (the pool was 9m in length), by the time we added on the structure for the balance tank, infinity edge collection at the far end of the pool and the traditional slatted pool cover pit (under the teak decking at the house end of the swimming pool), it occupied about one third of the garden.

PROJECT 'HAMPSTEAD'

To maintain garden space and planting, which was a key client requirement, it was decided to house the pool plant in an underground plant room.

The main contractor subsequently formed a watertight underground plant room at the end of the garden, which included pump, filter, ozone system and electric control panels.

Luckily the pool was fitted with a heat exchanger, which is significantly smaller than a boiler (600mm long x 200mm in diameter – normally cylindrical), which was heated via heating flows and returns from the house boiler. This meant the plant room could be kept very small – around 2.5m x 1.5m, also allowing for steps via an access hatch.

PROJECT 'HAMPSTEAD'

Project 'Hammersmith' was a 13.5m x 3m lap pool including bespoke grey and dark blended Italian glass mosaic throughout the pool interior, Italian grey limestone and teak decking surround. Pool includes a solar slatted automatic pool cover (housed in the far pool wall) and plant room with ozone disinfection concealed at the far end behind a cleverly designed curved white-painted render feature wall.

Although space is a restriction by virtue of boundary, through clever design and planning, clients' desires can usually be satisfied.

PROJECT 'HAMMERSMITH'

The ultimate small space solution is of course a moving floor swimming pool. This type of swimming pool offers dual use – when the moving floor is in the up position in an indoor pool hall, the pool hall can double up as a dance or yoga studio, play room for children, or a function room.

The same applies for a limited space garden or patio, where a moving floor can be fitted to an outdoor swimming pool. When the floor is up the patio can be used for sitting, and is deemed extremely safe (for children) as the floor is mechanically locked (via locking pins which locate into sleeves in the pool structure and 'pin' the floor into the up mode). For both the outdoor and indoor moving floor pool, when the floor is activated, and pulled down, it gently transforms into a swimming pool.

PROJECT 'NEWARK'

As described in the introductory chapters, the moving pool floor system is a floating stainless steel 'raft' with solid stainless steel top plate, that can be tiled to suit the client's choice. The pool itself always contains filtered and heated water, and is about 800mm deeper than the desired maximum pool water depth (the floor can be stopped at any level up to its maximum depth).

A hydraulic ram is bolted to the structural pool floor, which is attached to the floor raft via stainless steel chains. The raft itself is fitted with buoyancy packs, which make the floor float. When the chains are tort, the raft is held under the pool water and stowed in this 800mm bottom zone, when the floor is activated (from the down position into the up position) the chains are slowly released via the hydraulic ram, which allows the pool 'floor' to raise to the pool surface level and lock into position (via the locking pins). As the floor raises (about 10 minutes per metre), pool water percolates through a small gap between the moving floor and pool walls. Once up, and locked the pool floor can carry weights of 250kg / m² (or more if designed to do so), which is a lot!

The system is incredibly ingenious, and very desirable to overcome the small space pool location problem.

PROJECT 'NEWARK'

Project 'Newark' is one of the finest examples of a moving floor swimming pool that Guncast has been involved with. The client, Mrs. G, sets the scene:

"We have always had an indoor pool with this house, but often thought how wonderful it would be to have all that extra floor space to hand when the pool was not in use, particularly now, with four young spirited children to entertain.

Rather inspired and encouraged by a favourite old Hollywood movie, where the floor retracted to reveal a pool underneath, we consulted with our architect about the chances of us doing this ourselves, and he sensibly suggested we brought on board a pool consultant.

As well as doing our own research, we took advice from the experts, and ended up commissioning Guncast to install the Hydrofloors system from Belgium. This is one of the most tried and tested on the market, whereby the floor sinks and water runs in to fill the void.

It was quite a long job, as we were having a new kitchen installed at the same time, but there are no regrets, and we all absolutely love it.

The room is really multi functional, great for big parties of course, as it takes up to 120 comfortably. But particularly important for us, it also works as a sports and leisure area where we play badminton and run films from a projector. When the weather is bad, the children can still run around ad infinitum, burning off all that excess energy in a safe warm area, and this is great news for the rest of the house.

Yes of course the installation has been a topic of much fascination for our friends and neighbours, and everyone loves to see the transformation in action. But it works so well for us, and has enriched our quality of home life."

PROJECT 'NEWARK'

The clients required an indoor swimming pool but needed space for children to play and a yoga room. As with all London properties, project 'Newark' was not blessed with unlimited space, and therefore a moving floor swimming pool was a real proposition.

The concept was bourne to extend the main property backward (against and to the garden boundary walls) by building a single storey extension, which would be linked directly to the kitchen and family living space. This new extension was to house an indoor swimming pool with a moving floor. This may sound like a simple project, but when one factors in the plant space needed to filter the pool water and control the environment in the pool hall, and the fact the pool structure itself needed to be nearly 3m deep to accommodate the moving floor raft and to end up providing maximum 2m water depth - this is in fact a very complex build.

To achieve enough structural depth, the design team realised the zone in which the pool hall extension was to be built would need to be concrete piled before excavating down to about 4m. A perimeter of concrete piles was poured into bore holes around the working zone, over a period of about one month. Once hardened the excavation could commence safely and, at the same time, ensuring the existing building and garden walls would not collapse from being undermined.

Once the excavation was complete we formed within the larger 'hole' our sprayed concrete 10m x 5m x 3m (deep) swimming pool structure, which then sat against two sides of the larger 'hole'. A floor slab was then cast at floor level in the pool hall, which in effect created a basement area down one long and one short side of the pool structure (under the newly poured pool hall floor slab).

After several months work we had a swimming pool structure and a basement! At this point in time, a normal build sequence would see the pool hall building constructed, and the interior of the pool hall tiled and painted. We tiled the swimming pool structure in very large 600mm x 600mm porcelain tiles, and fitted the moving floor structure, which in this case was tiled as per the pool hall surround, in Italian limestone.

All the pool plant and equipment was installed - hidden away in the basement area - accessed via a discreet staircase built between the kitchen and pool hall. This also provided an area for a wine cellar, positioned ahead of the pool plant area, using a hidden door at the bottom of the staircase. All very chic.

PROJECT 'NEWARK'

From the photographs the quality of the selected materials is clear. The Italian limestone laid to the pool hall floor is one of the nicest I have ever seen. The feature wall which drops into the pool water is clad with 'pearl shell' mosaic, which we inset with pinpoint fibre optic lights. The sleek pool steps, which we formed from porcelain with foot treads set into the pool wall, with stainless steel pull handles; the discreet fibre optic strip light just under the pool coping; and fibre optics in the pool wall set in the centre of each tile – all this attention to detail helped to create one of the most stunning indoor swimming pools Guncast has ever had the chance to build.

There are two reasons, for me, why this particular project was such a success. Firstly, this was a moving floor project, and although Guncast has installed quite a few now – they are always special to undertake. Secondly, the standard of the selected finishing materials was very high quality and tasteful. The design team and contractors all delivered, but the people we really have to thank for realising this project as always, are the clients - especially so in this case.

PROJECT 'NEWARK'

chapter 6

'GARDENS OF DISTINCTION'

What makes a garden of distinction?

A truly impressive garden will often include incredible formal and informal planting, expansive lawns and meadows, intriguing paths that lead to hidden retreats, but will also showcase some form of water feature somewhere in the garden.

From the classic French Château with its fountains and waterfalls, to reflecting pools like the long thin pool that coolly reflects the Taj Mahal, to the Capability Brown lakes and ponds built into the stately home parks in England. A garden of distinction needs water to qualify!

Whilst garden design and landscape architecture are not new disciplines, the potential to create a swimming pool, which is in fact the water feature of the modern garden of distinction, is a relatively new concept.

The United Kingdom is blessed with two things, people who love and desire great gardens and an abundance of accomplished visionary garden designers and landscape architects, whose common goal is to create 'gardens of distinction' which more often than not includes a befitting swimming pool within the scheme.

I have worked with many clients, garden designers and landscape architects whose vision is to create a garden with subtle, natural deftness that must include a garden swimming pool.

This style of garden creation has really driven the reinvention of the garden swimming pool appearance to enhance a garden of distinction. The swimming pool must be subtle and natural; the back garden 'blue' is really not an option as the swimming pool has become the modern water feature and often the focal point of an architecturally designed garden.

Planting close to the pool itself softens the traditional hard paving around the pool and the pool finishing has become much darker to give the appearance of a natural pond or reflecting pool. Dark green or black mosaic can be used to achieve this effect or dark slates or porcelains of the same colour. Fountains, rills and waterfalls can also be incorporated into the swimming pool scheme to add the sound of running water to the sensory experience, relating back to the original water features in much older gardens.

As a team, Anthony Paul Landscape Architect, Brian Herbert of Outdoor Options Ltd and Guncast Swimming Pools have created a number of gardens of distinction, which include stunning swimming pools.

Project 'Arts and Crafts' in the grounds of a magnificent Surrey brick house with its well-proportioned solid forms, wide porches, steep roof, pointed window arches, brick fireplaces and wooden fittings, was such a scheme.

The client's brief was to add an outdoor swimming pool adjacent to the property within 'a natural boundary'. The area designated for the swimming pool abutted the west side of the house and overlooked a small meadow valley and onward south over the rolling Surrey Hills.

PROJECT 'ARTS AND CRAFTS'

Against such a backdrop, and adjacent to such an architecturally important and stylish property, the integration of the swimming pool into the grounds of the home was so important to get correct. Any design faux pas would be particularly disastrous and potentially downgrade the overall architectural excellence of the house and gardens.

Anthony Paul listened to the client's brief but also, when visiting the property for the first time, felt a sense of duty and obligation to design the most sympathetic in-keeping swimming pool and natural bordering gardens. He saw the proposal as a challenge, not only to ensure the project did not detract from the existing beauty, but to actually enhance and add to it.

The result was splendid. A flight of stairs from the front of the house down to the newly formed lower tier, comprising of large honed Yorkstone flag copings with bullnose edge, lining one side of the bottle green mosaic 14m long swimming pool.

The tiered garden drops away on the southern edge and it is here that natural grasses were planted to abut the swimming pool, making a natural boundary against winds and breezes for the meadow below. Slate shingle is laid on this edge to complete the break between pool structure and grasses.

Where the pool meets the wall of the property itself, there were some geometric shaped outbuildings built onto the side of the house, one of which was converted by Brian Herbert and his team into a changing room with shower. Another outbuilding at the meadow level was used as the plant room.

To complete the connection between the house and pool, decking was constructed at a slightly elevated level to the Yorkstone, making the scheme three dimensional and more interesting. This teak decking silvers with age and adds to the overall natural look, but also cleverly conceals the automatic pool cover in a traditional flooded cover pit at the shallow end of the pool.

PROJECT 'ARTS AND CRAFTS'

To complete the project a fountain that uses a specialised nozzle connected to a dedicated swimming pool pump was added. This draws pool water off the swimming pool circulation piping to create a jet from the deep end of the pool in a perfect arch over the pool, towards the shallow end. The nozzle itself was hidden underneath the York stone slabs at the end of the pool, so could not be seen, with the pump positioned in the plant room.

The scheme was an enormous success, not only complementing the property but enhancing the facilities and gardens for the client. The project was completed in 2008.

Brian Herbert from Outdoor Options Ltd comments:

"This arts and crafts property, set within panoramic Surrey views, was all about the drama and scale of the setting. The pool aspect slopes away from one end of the house opening out to large lawns and mature trees. Viewed from above, the use of strong planting groups and clean geometric lines to the hard landscape, produced a pool that architecturally sits well without competing with the bigger aspects, while also providing seclusion and protection from the wind.

To add feature to the pool, coloured blue LEDs were used along one side, producing vivid purple tones against the green glass mosaic tiles. Combining this with the arcing laminar flow water jet, the pool has a superb evening visual impact, as well as offering large sun decks to lounge upon in the day."

PROJECT 'ARTS AND CRAFTS'

Similar to 'Arts and Crafts' was project 'Vicarage', also in the Surrey Hills and for an old standing client who had previously had an outdoor swimming pool designed and constructed by the Anthony Paul and Guncast team.

Completed the year after project 'Arts and Crafts', project 'Vicarage' was delivered by the same team in a similar style. Buoyed up by our success with 'Arts and Crafts' and full of inspiration, Anthony Paul felt that this property needed an area of formal lawn as a transition and sitting area between the robust and proud Victorian vicarage and the outdoor swimming pool hidden but just visible through the newly planted foliage around the swimming pool area.

Although in the style of the arts and crafts pool, Brian Herbert and his team laid different materials around the pool, for uniqueness. The stone is light coloured sawn (six sided sawn – where top, bottom and all four sides are sawn to create smooth, even flags) Indian sandstone and the decking, which again forms the access into the pool area but also hides the flooded automatic pool cover pit for the slatted cover to the pool, was formed from another hardwood called Balau, which also silvers with age.

Forming the entrance zone to the swimming pool area, a warm material timber, invites the bather into the relaxation areas around the pool and, indeed, to swim in the pool itself.

Although we used the same bottle green mosaic to line the pool interior, this colour choice gives a natural green hue on sunny days and reflects on overcast days.

The pool is filtered and ozone disinfected, heated using an oil boiler and fitted with a solar gain enhancing slatted pool cover. The plant is hidden in the foliage behind the swimming pool in mature trees and newly planted ferns.

Guncast, Anthony Paul and Brian Herbert are well known for this style and, when we have worked together in the past, other similar demands have been met.

PROJECT 'VICARAGE'

Project 'Golf' was a substantial new build property in the neo classical style with a very mature garden, which abutted one of the more long established golf clubs, again with mature oaks. The garden in project 'Golf' was bordered by mature Rhododendron and was, in fact, a relatively awkward shape, as one of the adjacent golf club fairways wrapped around it. The client's brief was a swimming pool that was long enough to properly swim in, a building with kitchenette, shower, changing room and, of course, the pool plant room. The swimming pool also had to accommodate a fairly large, growing family.

In order to deliver such a swimming pool, there were several hurdles to overcome. The area where the property was sited had restrictive covenants on tree and plant removal, as well as tree protection orders. The client also wanted to maintain as much lawn as possible for family use and, due to the size of the deciduous trees, shade and leaves were an issue.

The Anthony Paul, Guncast and Brian Herbert team were challenged to deliver. We opted for a classic looking 13m long pool at the rear of the garden to maintain lawn space, avoid any need to remove trees (which was not permitted), maximise sun and minimise leaf deposit.

To exaggerate the classic look, the pool building was built at one end of the swimming pool and elevated. Tiered decking was constructed at the opposite end to create a seating and eating area. This elongated the scheme across the rear of the garden, again making it classical in appearance but not infringing on the valuable lawn space.

Logistically, the project was problematic. Access was to one side of the property with limited space and across the driveway, which the client needed permanent access to. All trees and root zones had to be cordoned off as heavy plant traversing over root zones can damage the trees. However, once into the working area, normal excavation and concrete spraying could take place.

PROJECT 'GOLF'

This was the first time that we used bottle green mosaic, which alters the appearance depending on the sun, cloud cover and, in this location, the effect of the trees shading onto the pool.

We were so pleased with the natural appearance of the swimming pool that we used the tile again at project 'Arts and Crafts' and project 'Vicarage'.

To complete this project and make it unique, we created a curving in of the swimming pool wall toward the shallow end. It not only curved in, but dropped down, forming a type of infinity edge, which over-spilled into a collection gully filled with small granite rocks. Again, this introduces into the scheme the sound of cascading water and is so unusual that I have never replicated this or seen it anywhere else in the world. I think it is fantastic.

The pool is slightly elevated out of the natural ground level on one edge, and the lawn side is lined with a very thin sawn stepping stone and slate shingle pathway on the opposite side.

Although leaves do drop in the autumn, they gather on the pool cover which exits from under the hardwood decking and can be blown off with a leaf blower.

Brian Herbert of Outdoor Options Ltd. comments:

"From the very outset, our client was aware that the installation of a pool at this property would be very visible from the house so it was imperative to have a sensitive design. Although it was a large garden for the area, to fit in a pool with pool building, the scale, placement, proportion, height and levels needed to be finely considered to ensure all the elements blended and naturally belonged to the setting.

As with most city installations, the restraints of access and logistics required meticulous planning. The design was produced by Anthony Paul Landscape Design, with Guncast Pools and Outdoor Options Ltd. (building and landscape) combining forces to create the pool, changing rooms with full facilities, along with every landscape aspect involved with blending them to their surroundings.

With close association to the house, all social aspects for use were considered: warm bright sun bathing areas, evening entertaining on a semi secluded circular deck, water feature aspects of the pool, plus stunning subtle lighting effects. These all combine for the enjoyment of this project, while also producing a wonderful pallet of soft tones and materials that create an aesthetic area to be viewed from all aspects."

PROJECT 'GOLF'

Not all clients require vision or help from landscape architects and garden designers. Some clients gravitate toward garden design as a past time and have an eye for detail.

One customer, at project 'Hamlet', owned two adjacent large country houses in the Oxfordshire region. Over the years, the customer took time and patience to landscape and plant the gardens and in the 1980's Guncast installed a swimming pool in the walled garden of the first house and then in the 2000's another swimming pool and reflecting rill, in the other property.

We photographed the newest of the two swimming pools at the time we completed in about 2008 and at the same time took the opportunity to photograph the older swimming pool (seen here on the left), which was still in excellent condition although in excess of twenty years old.

The beauty of these photographs is that both swimming pool schemes were surrounded in reclaimed Yorkstone and one can see how this looks when first laid and how it appears once aged further.

PROJECT 'HAMLET'

The original swimming pool was lined with a grey/white blend of Italian glass mosaic which makes the pool water appear blueish on sunny days, whereas the newer swimming pool was lined with bottle green mosaic and the adjacent reflecting rill in a pebble mosaic.

Whilst the older swimming pool functions perfectly well, the new swimming pool is fitted with modern embellishments such as ozone disinfection and a slatted solar gain enhancing pool cover at the far end of the swimming pool, under removable panels of flush fitted hardwood decking panels.

In both instances the concept and the design of the swimming pool integration into the wider garden scheme was the vision and, under the direction of the client himself, the hard landscaping around the pool was undertaken by a local Oxfordshire based landscape contractor, employed by the client.

In both instances these truly are gardens of distinction, featuring swimming pools as part of the overall garden design. However, by no means do the swimming pools dominate the gardens, in fact they are annexed to the gardens.

PROJECT 'HAMLET'

Another scheme that Guncast was appointed to be involved with, creating and constructing a swimming pool in the grounds of a very large modern new build house, was project 'Hans'.

The client worked closely with her developer, and between them they shared a vision of a large modern swimming pool to complement the new house. Both client and developer had strong feelings about what the end product would look like and were also very clear where the new swimming pool would be sited. It was decided that Guncast was the only addition needed to the team. Guncast designed and created the working drawings required to turn the dream of the client into a reality.

The rear garden immediately behind the house at project 'Hans' had a token planting scheme to cater for the period from when the house was first constructed to phase two of the project, which would be the new outdoor swimming pool.

Our scope of works included removing the existing soft and hard landscaping, excavating, designing and constructing not only the swimming pool structure but the surround structural slab and retaining walls – which were all built using sprayed concrete.

The 15m long pool was lined with Anthracite grey glass mosaic. It included ozone disinfection and a solar slatted automatic pool cover under the decking at the far end of the pool.

For the surround paving and cladding to the retaining wall, we worked with a company called Stoneage, a well known supplier of limestone and marble. The grey stone around the pool and the matching pool coping was supplied by Stoneage and is a moleanos limestone from Portugal, which is a nice even grey colour called Pietra Serena. The cladding to the retaining wall is generally Pietra Serena with the cladding to the recessed bays in Porta D limestone. The overall effect is modern and complements the existing property and the client's tastes.

PROJECT 'HANS'

Another modern addition to the scheme was that the pool was heated using a ground source heat pump system which, in 2006 when this pool was built, was the first experience we'd had with ground source heat pumps.

Loops of pipe work containing circulating water and biodegradable glycol fluid are laid into excavated horizontal trenches about 1.5m below ground level or into vertical bore holes. The ambient temperature of the sub soil at this level is constant all year round at about 10°C and the water circulating through the buried pipework will slowly absorb this latent heat, which is extracted via a buffer tank in the plant room.

The water in the buffer tank will warm (and can be heat boosted), and in turn can be connected to a heat exchanger that is connected to the swimming pool circulation pipework.

It struck me at the time that the warm water being created in this way is consistent in terms of availability (i.e. not affected by lack of sun as a solar thermal system is, or by lack of warm air as an air source heat pump is). Also, the temperature of the warm water generated by this system (about 40°C) is in harmony with the typical water temperatures for an outdoor swimming pool (about 28°C).

Therefore, at the time, I saw this as potentially being the optimum solution for heating an outdoor swimming pool, in terms of carbon foot print and expenditure, fossil fuels and low noise levels.

However, heat pumps are expensive to install in the first instance and because they run using electricity (which is not the cheapest form of energy), if the owner starts to use the electricity to increase the temperature of the primary water in the buffer tank, then the system becomes incrementally more costly to run. It is, therefore, essential that any heat pump system is designed to provide maximum efficiency, which is achieved through quality of product and through quality of the calculations for energy transfer in the ground. A well specified system can heat a pool for around half the cost of oil or LPG.

Whether expensive to install or not, there has been a trend toward using green energy sources and, although perhaps ground source heat pumps did not turn out to be quite the optimum pool heating solution that I thought at the time, we have fitted many more. This is mainly because some customers like to feel that the carbon footprint of owning and heating a swimming pool is mitigated to a degree by heating the swimming pool using this method.

PROJECT 'HANS'

Other influential landscape architects that Guncast has worked with are the combined Mary Keen and Pip Morrison team. With a number of swimming pools built for Pip and Mary in their clients' gardens of distinction, with their bold statements, strong planting schemes and imposing hard landscaping with enormous Portland stone flagstones - one that was highly demanding in terms of construction sequence was project 'Banbury'.

The client brief was for a 20m long outdoor swimming pool with a diving end, tucked away in what was previously a formal planting area between a very large garden wall (some 3.5m high) and a very well established Yew hedge. Although the designated area was long enough to easily accommodate the 20m swimming pool, the width was an issue at 8m maximum and the wall or Yew hedge could not be disturbed.

To make matters more complicated, the access into the working zone was via an adjacent field (not owned by the client), passed a small pond, through garden paths and around trees (with tree protection orders on them). Another dimension of complexity was added to the logistics of the build when the pool excavation zone turned out to be in an area of garden with an unusually high water table / running water.

Having agreed access across the adjacent field with the owner, via a hired-in aluminium track way, and protection of the trees and the root zones with an agreed system of laying bark chippings on terram matting, we traversed into the working area only with small machinery and proceeded to excavate for the pool.

Realising during the design process, and by excavating by hand a small trial pit at the base of the garden wall, we quickly established that the garden wall had foundations, but only to a depth of about 1m. This meant that by excavating for the pool as close as 2m from the base of the garden wall, we would be undermining the garden wall footings (risking collapse). Furthermore, once the pool structure was built, the garden wall would be too close above the invert level of the pool structure and would impose additional loads into the structure of the pool wall that would normally need to be factored into the structural engineer's calculations.

Having foreseen this in the design stage, we planned to undertake a system of underpinning where we excavated 1m sections under the garden wall down to the full excavation depths and sprayed reinforced gunite concrete against these banks of excavation. By doing this in small segments at a time, we were able to effectively create a reinforced retaining wall against the earth under the garden wall foundations to protect against undermining and potential collapse and allow works and excavation to proceed safely.

Although the proposed system was successful, the process was slow, compounded by removing the soil in very small dumper trucks via pathways and to the far side of the field, but also the ground water was far worse than anticipated and quite a lot worse than we'd encountered before or since. As soon as the initial excavation began on site and the extent of the ground water problem was discovered, we managed the water by digging deep 'well points' into the ground around the swimming pool excavation zone. Each well was lined with a large bore drainage pipe and a submersible pump was lowered down and left pumping 24 hours a day to draw away the ground water, which was pumped down to the client's pond.

With the ground water managed and the excavation complete, the normal construction process begun.

PROJECT 'BANBURY'

The 20m long by 4m swimming pool was constructed using sprayed concrete and then lined with large 900mm x 450mm structured black porcelain slabs. The York stone surround and copings were sourced by Pip Morrison from a reclamation yard and the whole effect created a dramatic swimming pool surrounded by the dominating garden wall and aged Yew hedge, which remained untouched by the serious civil engineering works that took place in between them.

The swimming pool ended up 2.2m deep to accommodate safe diving and was fitted with a solar slatted swimming pool cover, concealed in the deep end wall.

The adjacent existing buildings, which had a redundant basement, were renovated by Pip and Mary. The client's builders managed to access the basement and waterproof render throughout, enabling us to use this area for the swimming pool equipment. Whilst the area was very compact and accessible via a floor hatch and specially designed staircase, we were able to use this space, meaning no further building was needed, or space lost, to house the pool plant.

Landscape Architect Mary Keen comments:

"One of our favourite and most successful pools had to be fitted into a space 30m long and only 8m wide, contained by a high sunny brick wall with an old garden house opening off it and an existing Yew hedge.

The client had asked for a pool in an area just outside the garden where compost heaps and chickens were kept, but the suntrap under an 18th century wall with a beautifully trained pear seemed to us a much happier site and the garden house made an unobtrusive pool house.

Of course there were problems. The pool occupied half the width of the site and almost three quarters of its length with paving round it, but we like long lap pools best.

We knew the wall would need some underpinning and that proved tense, but worst of all was that the water table was high enough to flood the construction so badly that a pump had to be kept going for months through a wet winter. It was a triumph by Guncast to deliver such a beautiful porcelain slate lined pool that, in the end, looked as though it had always been there. The pear with Iris at its feet continued to flourish and even the Yew hedge stood up to the massive operation of fitting a high tech pool into a very small and potentially fragile space."

PROJECT 'BANBURY'

English gardens featuring York stone and full of naturalistic planting are very much the staple of Ian Smith from 'Acres Wilds' who has created some impressive gardens.

Working together in the early 2000's on project 'Barn Owl', Guncast was commissioned by the passionate owner of this major garden remodelling project, to build the swimming pool in a garden enclave adjacent to the main house.

Whilst the swimming pool and the surrounding landscape would normally be considered major works, really in this instance this was only a small percentage of the work Ian and the client were committed to. Major relevelling of the lower fields, installation of lakes and the laying and tree lining of the half mile driveway, were other works running in tandem with the pool, but did not mean Ian's critical eye or the hands-on client overlooked the swimming pool and spa area.

One of the styles of Acres Wild is to plant close to one boundary of the swimming pool; in this case it was lavender. This was actually quite clever as it is not only very pleasant to swim close to planting in this fashion, but saves paving an area one might not necessarily ever use and also means the swimming pool can be pushed to one side creating a wider seating and large useable space to the other side.

I also love the three dimensional aspect of this project, which lifts and makes the whole area much more interesting. The raised timber decking over the pool cover pit abuts a stone clad retaining wall at an even higher level, which in turn, leads to the raised overflowing spa (in this case the hydro spa shell was PVC and pre-tiled prior to delivery, as per the swimming pool). The hydro spa pool was deck level, which we overflowed via underground piping back to the swimming pool, meaning that the spa and pool were heated and filtered by a shared system. The spa is transferred into dedicated use via a switch adjacent to the spa. This activates automatic valves and dedicates the heating and filter system only to the spa for two hours (and then switches back), allowing the spa to heat up to the correct temperature.

In Acres Wild 'style', the surround was Yorkstone as was the pool coping and spa capping, which was butt jointed (not pointed) allowing little green mosses and tiny flowers to peak through the joints making for the stone surround paving to look incredibly natural in a very short period of time. The timber pergola overlooking the lower fields frames the whole area, allowing creeper plants to grow and shield against any breeze.

PROJECT 'BARN OWL'

Ian Smith of Acres Wild comments:

"Project 'Barn Owl' is located in a very rural part of East Sussex, close to Brightling Down, one of the highest points in the 'High Weald'. With glorious and extensive views west over meadows, woodland and distant downland, you can literally watch the weather come in. The price to pay for this lofty and highly desirable location is exposure to wind and a relatively poor and heavy clay soil. The site slopes from east to west, with the house located in the centre of the plot and extensive woodland to the north and south. Previously the farm had been a small single storey dwelling, with no garden to speak of, and a collection of farm outbuildings.

The clients bought the property with the intention of building a new house, extensively using reclaimed materials to create a 'Traditional Sussex Farmhouse' that would fit seamlessly into its location, with a suitably inspiring landscape design to complement and enhance the house. The most important factor was that the house and garden should look as though they had always been there, seeking to create a sense of permanence and comfortable ageing, whilst accommodating 'modern' features, such as the swimming pool, in a sensitive and subtle way.

The swimming pool garden needed to be close to the house and also sheltered from the prevailing winds, so a space between the house and a cluster of existing outbuildings was chosen as the ideal location. This space provided an opportunity to design a courtyard like setting for the pool with walls and a pergola structure added to give additional privacy and shelter, plus the opportunity to use one of the outbuildings for the pool plant. The space was designed to be a discreet area within the overall garden plan, but still connected to the rest of the garden and the landscape beyond.

The site for the pool was gently sloping and this was exploited to nestle the pool into the garden and to create a small decked area at the end of the pool which also provides access to the pool cover pit. As space was limited the swimming pool was paved on two sides, creating a terrace with sufficient space for a table and sun loungers and a raised area for a bench overlooking the pool and a discreetly placed spa. The remaining sides of the pool were planted with appropriate easy care plants to soften the space and provide visual interest. A pergola covered walkway forms the south boundary of the swimming pool garden giving access to the rest of the garden and also providing shelter to the pool, whilst allowing framed views out to the wider landscape. Natural materials including reclaimed brick and York stone give a sense of comfortable age to the garden and the swimming pool coping is made with sawn York stone to provide a practical and attractive edge that blends seamlessly with the rest of the garden.

The garden does not shout 'design', but the input of careful and considered garden design principles was essential in underpinning the experience of project 'Barn Owl' and the sense that it has simply always been there.

This garden won the 2007 Sussex Heritage Trust Landscape and Gardens Award and the Best Large Residential Garden in the 2012 Society of Garden Designers Awards."

Inspiration for other projects, when it comes to the style of the swimming pool itself, comes from my travels and experiences.

Project 'Japan' was really borne from a trip to Tokyo and Kyoto and the zen gardens with little running pebbled streams that can be seen as part of landscaping in the cities.

Whilst the clients who commissioned project 'Japan' had a clear idea what they were going to build (e.g. a 14m long swimming pool and modern pool house with facilities such as changing room, lounge area, kitchenette and showers etc), the style of swimming pool was undecided.

I put forward a design idea and, as it happened, the clients had a strong liking for Japanese styles and architectures.

I really wanted to aim for a dark tiled reflective swimming pool with grey limestone and grey or silvered hardwood decking. The other essential aspect of this project as far as I was concerned was the infinity edge to one long side to recreate the sound of trickling water, as is often heard in Japan. This was to be lined with grey Java pebble mosaic and to incorporate up lighting, shining toward the pool overflow wall.

My Japanese inspired concept was endorsed by the client and we agreed the design was to feature anthracite black mosaic inside the swimming pool, Pietra Serena grey limestone pool copings to the pool edging and a small patio area at the shallow end. There were Java pebbles in the overflow rill and teak decking to one side of the swimming pool and over the automatic pool cover flooded pit (you can see this is under the raised decking at the pool house end of the pool).

The graded lawns around this pool, the simple pool house architecture and the Japanese inspired swimming pool, in my opinion make this a true 'garden of distinction'.

PROJECT 'JAPAN'

Some garden designers take the natural looking swimming pool one stage further and actually commission the installation of a natural swimming pool, which circulates the natural pool water via a pump up into a reed bed, naturally cleansing the water to a degree that is safe for bathing. The pool water percolates through the reeds then back into the swimming pool.

Although we have not constructed any natural swimming pools with reed beds, which is not our area of expertise, we have constructed a number of 'natural looking rock pools' that at first appearance look like a natural pool or pond. This is achieved by disguising the swimming pool with dark tiles or dark marbelite inside the pool and using boulders or rocks as the edging or coping, which in turn can be stacked or piled up to form a waterfall.

Project 'Rock Pool' was such a project and was lined internally with dark mosaic and rocks around to create the illusion of a natural swimming pool. In its own way and uniqueness, the pool with its inviting running water and seclusion in the corner of garden, relates back to all the desirable design elements of water in a garden of distinction.

PROJECT 'ROCK POOL'

chapter 7

'FAMILY'

The majority of swimming pools installed into domestic properties are built for the owner's pleasure, but the principal behind the purchase will include factors that relate to all-round family use and being able to use the swimming pool facility for many different activities.

As an example, one member of the family may wish to use the swimming pool for exercise and laps, but the family may include younger members (requiring a shallow pool or steps that toddlers can splash play on). It may include teenagers that like to dive and jump in (requiring a deep end), or indeed the elderly who simply like to sit in a warm zone and observe (spa pool).

The result is that many multifunctional swimming pools are built – which I describe as family pools, simply because they cater for all and sundry. The more all-round the facilities, the more the family and friends will use the swimming pool.

A prime example of an all-round luxury 'family' swimming pool is project 'Chester'.

The client was no stranger to owning swimming pools and, with quite a large family, managed to secure an amazing Georgian property, prime for development.

The project was a complete refurbishment of the property to include an underground basement extension positioned mostly under one side of the property / garden area, but to be connected to the existing basement.

The new basement area was designed so that cleverly used rooflights channelled natural daylight down from the garden above, but there was also access via a stairway over the shallow end of the pool into a sunken garden. A combination of white ceilings and walls to the interior of the pool hall and a very light coloured natural limestone to the pool hall floor and pool copings, resulted in a very light and airy setting, which can be difficult to achieve in a basement.

The client's brief was to include a swimming pool long enough for exercise and laps, with an automatic pool cover, a shallow end for smaller children and less confident swimmers and a deep end for racing dives and jumping in. A raised hydro spa pool was required to accommodate six bathers and to overlook the main pool, as well as a steam room, sauna and adjacent cold water plunge pool (which bathers immerse themselves in after using the sauna and / or steam room). A gym area partitioned by a glazed screen, with a slightly cooled atmosphere (as the main pool hall's heated atmosphere would be too warm for gym workouts), was also required.

The client specified that the swimming pool, spa pool and cold plunge were to be run with as little chlorine as possible. Although not as strong a disinfectant as chlorine, we decided to run all three pools via automatic dosing systems, which would use hydrogen peroxide, added once a week to disinfect the water in all three pools with the support of secondary disinfection, ozone. pH was adjusted with sodium bisulphate and dosing pumps.

Although chlorine is added by virtue of the incoming town's water and periodic 'super chlorination' (which is necessary to kill the more resilient bugs and bacteria), the pool water generally has very low chlorine levels and the result is that the pool hall and water is virtually odourless. Having walked into so many pool halls where a lingering smell is present, it is almost bizarre to enter a pool hall where the presence of chlorine cannot immediately be detected.

The layout was developed by the client's architect, Andrew Harper of Holden Harper, and Guncast was appointed by the main contractor GMD to design and construct the three pools, sauna and steam room.

PROJECT 'CHESTER'

Although the basement and pool hall were important aspects of the overall project, they were only a small section of a very large refurbishment, which took nearly two years, but ran very smoothly.

The only real complication with the project was the design team's concern that the pool area and house would be used to the absolute maximum by the family on Christmas day. So much electricity would be drawn to serve all the facilities in one go (both steam room and sauna require very large electrical supplies), that a fail safe 'trip out' would occur, and calling out an electrical engineer on Christmas day is not easily done! So, we developed another separate, smaller, incoming electrical supply that served the pool cover, air handling unit / pool and pool hall heating system that would remain live if the incoming electrical main was to trip out.

The whole scheme is one that I am particularly proud of delivering to a client who knew, having owned swimming pools before, exactly what they wanted and ended up with a fabulous facility for the whole family.

Richard Holden comments:

"The property consists of a statutory listed house and garden that underwent extensive alteration and restoration.

The pool building is connected to the other leisure and recreational facilities at the basement level of the existing building. This new structure was constructed in reinforced concrete and so designed that the garden flowed over its roof, with concealed skylights lighting the pool area below.

An area of large glazing overlooking a sunken planted water cascade connects the pool to the garden. The pool has associated facilities of a spa and sauna and is visually connected to the adjacent gym by a faceted glass screen. User controlled lighting was employed to vary the night time abeyance."

PROJECT 'CHESTER'

'East Meets West' is another project that shares the same all-round family facilities as project 'Chester' but in a totally different style. The main pool was a grand 12m x 7.5m with a constant depth of 1.2m (as diving was not required). An automatic pool cover was required in a floor chamber at one end of the swimming pool (concealed under a tiled frame), and a splash / paddling area attached to the swimming pool, cold plunge pool, hydro spa pool, sauna and steam room were also specified.

Whilst the filtration and heating plant were virtually identical to project 'Chester', the appearance of the swimming pool, tiling scheme and method of heating the swimming pool were totally different.

The clients, keen yoga and relaxation enthusiasts, wanted a modern, clean, calm pool hall for meditation and relaxation, but also required the pool to be a facility for all when not being used for yoga. The clients also had a strong environmentalist ethos and wanted the pool hall and its facilities to be carbon neutral.

From the photographs it is clear to see that the client's brief was met by architects James Rae and Duncan Baker-Brown of BBM Sustainable Design Ltd, who worked alongside Guncast to deliver a simple but effective tiling scheme.

Using 600mm x 300mm grey-green porcelain tiles and preformed pool copings, we laid the tiles so that they ran seamlessly across the pool hall floor, following the same pattern in and out of all three pools. Using one material in this fashion is very 'easy on the eye' and I think calms the atmosphere.

The pools were to be set into a newly built 'barn' building in the location of an old portal frame and corrugated iron hay barn, in the grounds of the client's farm.

PROJECT 'EAST MEETS WEST'

With a high vaulted ceiling and white wash plaster walls, the architects created an airy pool hall, which again adds to the relaxed feel. The contrast between the white walls and ceilings and grey-green tiles, achieves a modern twist. Rooflights above the pool and windows at various levels throughout the pool hall introduce natural light and really complete the ambience.

Very conscious of trying to achieve a carbon neutral facility, the client not only appointed BBM, known for creating carbon neutral buildings, but also sought the expert advice of Mark Robinson, from Robinson Associates, which is a field leading company in energy conservation and reduction.

Although Guncast has been involved with many swimming pools heated by a green energy source, Mark planned to use another barn in the fields of the client's farm as an intelligent energy centre. By using a combination of a wood pellet boiler and ground source, energy is created on demand as needed and it never over produces. This effective, efficient and low carbon emission method of producing heated water to power the swimming heat exchangers, is only one part of the equation.

By insulating the swimming pool, the pool hall floor, barn walls and roof construction with very high quality extruded polystyrene 200mm – 300mm thick, heat losses are totally reduced. We also linked the automatic pool cover to the air handling unit so that once the pool is covered, the pool hall air temperature drops, reducing the amount of moisture in the pool hall. This automatically slows the internal fan in the air handling unit, reducing the amount of heating required from the energy centre and electricity used.

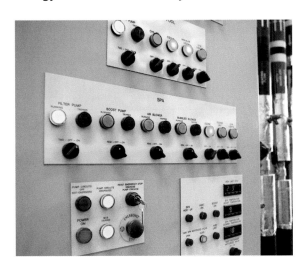

All circulation pumps are fitted with timers so that they run for the absolute minimum time necessary and where possible the pumps are at a variable speed, slowing to tick over rate in down time.

The combined efforts of the team resulted in a swimming pool facility which is about as efficient as can be achieved on such a luxurious installation.

PROJECT 'EAST MEETS WEST'

James Rae of BBM Architects comments:

"In 2008 BBM Sustainable Design Ltd was commissioned to design a scheme for a new contemporary country house set in the stunning Sussex Weald. The project also involved the restoration of a poorly converted listed oast house and the design of a new pool house as well as a landscape appraisal and contemporary landscape scheme designed by Studio Engleback.

The landscape design included a new outdoor 'natural' swimming pool with a reed bed. The project was of further interest as the client shared BBM's commitment to low carbon development. With an estate of 275 acres, including 150 acres of standing woodland the project is well able to become self-sufficient from the point of view of energy. With this in mind BBM designed an independent energy centre for the site that creates energy from biomass sourced from our client's estate and stores energy captured from the sun's energy.

The master plan for the site allowed for the development works to be undertaken in two phases, the first of which delivered the heated swimming pool with its hot and cold pools plus sauna and steam room in tandem with the restoration of the listed oast house, the natural pool and energy centre.

The pool house replaced a derelict dairy building dating from the 1940s. One of the planning constraints imposed on the scheme was that the new pool house should match the form and volume of this building, hence the agricultural feel of this very high spec building.

The pool house is constructed with the most environmentally friendly materials where possible, such as a timber framed structure, insulation made from waste timber fibre, and locally sourced sweet chestnut cladding. Chestnut cladding is used for the swimming pool's beautiful curved ceiling. The internal walls are hand finished in a breathable plaster called 'tadelakt', a technique from Morocco. This material was specified as it has been used for centuries in Turkish baths and is very well suited to the particular conditions a heated pool creates. It is self-finished requiring no decorating, while providing a particularly sensuous depth and tactile feel to the pool house interior.

Natural light is manipulated via a series of rooflights positioned to make best use of sunlight throughout the day, and can also be used to passively ventilate and cool the space during the summer months, reducing the mechanical load of the building. Seemingly frameless large windows and doors have been positioned to take advantage of beautiful views across adjacent meadows. The east west axis is emphasised by framing the main window with a pair of 5m high opal glass screens that locate and provide privacy to a spa pool and cold plunge pool respectively.

Changing rooms have rooflights with 3.5m tall light funnels ensuring that all parts of this complex have natural light and ventilation. Floors throughout are finished with a textured porcelain tile.

Although an energy-hungry element on site, we have ensured that the fabric of the Pool House is super insulated with up to 400mm of insulation in the roof and 320mm in the walls. It is also super air tight achieving a minuscule air permeability of 3m³ per m² at 50 PA external pressure (to put this into context, the current Local Authority Building Control requirement for a new build house is 10m³ per m²).

These features ensure that the carbon neutral energy generated by the onsite energy centre is not wasted. The north side of the pitched roof is finished in a mat of sedum plants with the south side completed with a large 8.61kW array of photovoltaic solar panels, generating electricity for the building as well as a 8no solar thermal panels. All pool equipment was carefully specified to be as energy efficient as possible."

PROJECT 'EAST MEETS WEST'

A 'family' swimming pool is not limited to an indoor swimming pool and spa, with all the additional facilities such as sauna and steam room. To qualify, it may simply be an outdoor swimming pool which has been designed with the family as the centre of attention.

Project 'Marryat' is such a swimming pool. Guncast originally built the swimming pool in the 1990s but it was refurbished for the new owners of the property in about 2010. Whilst the original swimming pool structure was re-used (12m x 6m x 3m deep), the client wanted to add an adjacent pool building with changing room, showers, toilets, a pool lounge, and also a hydro spa pool to the scheme. As well as this, the swimming pool itself was remodelled and the old Roman end steps were broken out to make the pool more contemporary in appearance.

Guncast was appointed by developer, Peter Mercieca, to remodel the swimming pool and construct the hydro spa pool, whilst his team concentrated on the construction of the modern pool building.

The key to the success of this project and making this an all-round family facility, was the pool building itself. Whilst we are proud of the swimming pool and spa (and having been the original builder of the swimming pool appreciated the opportunity to undertake this work), the construction of the pool building which provided all modern luxuries and conveniences adjacent to the swimming pool and spa at the bottom of a very large garden, really made the scheme a family swimming pool.

Project 'Clapham' was built around the same time as project 'Marryat' and was for a young family with small children. The unusual infinity end to the swimming pool and the very contemporary building creates an award winning designed indoor swimming pool.

The 'wow factors' are the listed flint wall, which originally formed the first section of garden wall, and the enormous sliding glass doors.

The client's brief to Neil Etheridge of Simon Morray-Jones Architects was for a contemporary family swimming pool that joined onto the existing property, enabling direct access between both buildings.

Neil was forward thinking and managed to develop a scheme that left intact the listed garden wall and used a cluster of existing outbuildings to connect up and create an indoor pool, which was effectively built as a 'lean to' against the garden wall. The outbuildings were joined up and formed the walk way from the main property and provided changing rooms and showers.

To the rear of the listed flint garden wall was another almost derelict two storey 'shed' which was built as an existing 'lean to' on the opposite side of the pool hall or new 'lean to'. This made the perfect plant room to house the pool filtration and air handling units on the upper level.

Utilising the existing buildings in this way and leaving the listed garden wall untouched, was a sympathetic proposal and was well received by the local planning authorities. Although a complex build which required skilled craftsmen, an extremely well architecturally planned indoor pool was built for the client and their family by the team.

The large sliding glass doors, which completely open the pool hall to the exterior paved area, is the real element that makes this a family pool. Being able to open and enlarge the facility in this way means the garden and play areas are clearly visible from the pool, and vice versa.

Effectively, the indoor and outdoor areas blur into one, which to me is hugely desirable.

PROJECT 'CLAPHAM'

Neil Etheridge of Simon Morray-Jones Architects comments:

"The origins of the house date back to the early 18th century and the property was extensively remodelled and extended in the late Georgian / Regency period with the garden enclosed by a beautiful flint and brick wall in the Sussex vernacular. The property is also of historic significance as it was reported to have been visited on numerous occasions by the Prince Regent. Serious thought, therefore, had to be given to the historic buildings and their setting in preparation of the design and it was essential that the new building would not compete, in scale or architecturally, with the listed house.

Our minimalist approach to the building design, together with a selection of brick and flint walling, terned stainless steel roof structure and large glazing panels, provides an unashamedly contemporary building whilst being respectful of the scale and character of the environment.

There was clear evidence of an earlier building on the site of the new pool building (confirmed by the Ordnance Survey Map of 1874) so it was felt appropriate, after discussions with the Local Authority Conservation Officer, that the new building be positioned in that location. The site was in the least obtrusive position within the walled garden and could not be seen from any other properties or the nearby public footways.

The adjacent structure (to the north side of the garden wall) was also ideal for housing air handling equipment, pool pumps and filters without the need for any other new structures. The 'Dairy' building had been converted in the late 20th century but the detailing was rather poor and in need of remedial attention. This structure was, therefore, incorporated into the new pool complex to provide a convenient link from the inner courtyard and main house.

Consideration had to be given to treatment of differing floor levels between the inner courtyard up to the garden area (and pool deck level) so a lower flat-roofed link housing a small changing / shower area was included, incorporating steps up to the pool deck.

The planning consent required the historic garden wall to be retained and the clients were also keen for this to be featured within the main pool. This did, however, lead to technical difficulties as the old wall could not be put under further load, nor could it be taken down and rebuilt during construction (leading to complicated propping and underpinning). The structural steel support to the terned stainless steel roof, therefore, had to be designed to span onto a heavy steel beam adjacent to the old flint wall which, to achieve a clear span, became a very deep section. The flint wall could not be raised (again for planning reasons) so this also added further complications to achieve the maximum ceiling height in the main pool room.

The client was also very keen to pursue green, energy-efficient heating to the pool and structure, so state-of-the-art high temperature electric heat pumps were employed in conjunction with photovoltaic solar panels (positioned some distance from the buildings).

The contemporary approach to the design was carefully considered to complement the historic setting. Use of matching flint and brick walling blends with the garden wall to create a seamless transition between building structure and garden. The large glazed screen is fully retractable which, on (admittedly rare) warm days, makes it feel like an outdoor pool. This was a major consideration for the clients as they have a young family and were keen for the pool, terrace and garden spaces to flow into each other. The selection of the natural stone floor finish was, therefore, really important as it had to work aesthetically (and practically) both internally and externally."

PROJECT 'CLAPHAM'

There is nothing more rewarding than swimming as an exercise, which combines having fun with family. Watching my own children as they have learnt to swim and, as they have got older, splashing and playing for hours on end, is a wonderful experience. Throughout my childhood we were always lucky enough to own a swimming pool and I remember even on the coldest days using the swimming pool endlessly.

Projects 'Priory' and 'Blanche' really made me reminisce on my own experiences, having completed both projects for the same family.

The first of the two projects was project 'Priory', built circa 2008 as part of a refurbishment project on an enormous scale. The façade and walls to the property were to be retained as a planning requirement, but the rest of the house was demolished and rebuilt to accommodate a basement with a large indoor deck level swimming pool, sauna and steam room, as well as wine store, therapy rooms, cinema, study, gym, plant rooms (for pool, house and internal electronic management and control system), toilets, showers and changing rooms.

The whole basement area was in excess of 4000ft² and the project took around two years to complete.

The result was adding not only a huge additional area of useable space, but space that was defined as family areas. The swimming pool itself was 13mx 4m, with a deep end and was the centre piece to the 'spa area'. To add to the boutique spa feel we added a variable speed waterfall and pump to the staggered slate feature wall, which can either trickle or flow down into the pool water.

The clients, who are keen on interior design, created a mellow colour scheme of natural white and grey slates and limestone, which are enriched by the natural light streaming from the sliding doors into the sunken garden at one end of the pool hall or the rooflights.

PROJECT 'PRIORY'

Whilst we were very lucky to be involved with such a satisfying project as project 'Priory', we were subsequently invited to work on the client's private villa project 'Terre'.

Here the swimming pool was to be the focal point of the villa's walled gardens and outdoor sitting and lounge spaces, and therefore central to outdoor family living. To be involved with this was a pleasure for me and was to be a project of grand proportion.

The villa itself is extremely grand and proud looking; the swimming pool had to match. First was the size – there was no compromise here at 18m x 6m with water deep enough for diving.

As can be seen from the photographs, this is in keeping with the space allocated for the swimming pool and is in total proportion to the buildings around.

The swimming pool was lined with Italian black structured porcelain that I had sourced. At first I thought it might possibly be a bit austere; but again the client's eye for design prevailed, as this most definitely works in the sense of reflective pools designed into gardens of distinction. The fossilised grey Portuguese copings, which are 100mm thick, complement the tiling scheme and their size is in keeping with the overall grand statement.

A year or two after project 'Terre' was completed, I travelled to see the client when he was at the villa with his family. It was a warm day and the family was relaxing by the swimming pool with guests; the children and teenagers were swimming totally carefree in the pool. This really sums up the way a family pool should be used.

PROJECT 'TERRE'

Often, building a pool for a client and their family is very rewarding, as for a lot of people, to own a swimming pool is the epitome of luxury and several clients have told me it has 'changed their lives for the better'.

chapter 8

'HEALTH AND FITNESS'

Hydrotherapy and Vitality Swimming Pools.

Hydrotherapy by definition is the use of water for pain relief, curing and treatment. In the context of swimming pool construction, Hydrotherapy relates to swimming pools specifically constructed for patients to be immersed in water for therapeutic reasons.

Hydrotherapy is an all encompassing word that involves all sorts of water treatments which take advantage of human buoyancy (whilst in water for physiotherapy) and water temperature (hot and cold) to stimulate blood circulation. Consequently, many ailments are treated this way and I myself once had Hydrotherapy at my local hospital for a slipped disc in my back.

Whilst hydrotherapy (originally called Hydropathy) proliferated in the 1900's throughout Europe and America, it is only in the last 50 years or so that we've seen the development of associated hydrotherapy type pools really aimed for the home owner to have fitted at their property.

In particular, hydro spa baths and hot tubs are not an uncommon sight, ranging from the luxury basement private swimming pools to boutique hotels, which include vitality swimming pools with massage stations, bubble pads, massage benches and powerful massage jets.

The advent of these new types of swimming pools and spas has really split hydrotherapy swimming pools into two factions: hydrotherapy for therapeutic treatment and hydrotherapy for leisure.

In both cases the swimming pool tends to be relatively small, as swimming itself is not an activity that is pursued in these pools.

A typical size (if there is one) would be around 6m x 4m x 1000mm/1200mm deep and in both cases the pool water is warmer than a 'swimming' pool, ranging from 34°C up to 38°C.

By virtue of the fact that hydrotherapy pools have high temperature water and possibly sick patients using the water (both of which are a concern for bacteria prevention and disinfection), it is preferable and defined by bodies such as PWTAG (Pool Water Treatment Advisory Group) that the filtration cycle for a hydrotherapy swimming pool should not exceed 1 ½ hours, and in some cases should be 30 minutes.

In layman's terms, this means that the filtration systems used to drive these swimming pools are very large (physically and in terms of capacity) in comparison to the size of the pool and how much filtration and treatment the pool requires. Not only is the filtration system large, but it is paramount that the pool water is disinfected to a high degree as it would be counterproductive for an already sick patient to end up in a worse condition after using the pool.

It is also highly desirable (if not essential) that the pool water is as low as possible in primary disinfectant (normally chlorine being the most effective disinfectant for the job in hand), so that the swimming environment is as pleasant as possible, particularly for hydrotherapists who spend long periods of time in the water. This is achieved by commercial grade ultra violet or ozone (sometimes a combination of both) disinfection being fitted to ease the burden on the chlorine, thus allowing the pool water to be run at much lower than normal chlorine levels.

For special needs schools and centres where the users of the hydrotherapy pool can be physically and / or mentally impaired, it would be expected that the swimming filtration and treatment system would be of the highest possible specification that finances for the project allow.

At such a special needs centre in Bordon, Guncast worked very closely with Hampshire County Council to design and construct a hydrotherapy swimming pool which would be heavily used by children, working with trained hydrotherapists who spend long periods in the pool water with patients, moving their limbs and muscles for physiotherapy.

Whilst the swimming pool was functional and municipal in appearance and was approximately 6m x 4.5m x 1200mm deep, the behind the scenes filtration system was extremely high specification.

With an outline performance specification written and provided by Hampshire County Council, the swimming pool had a deck level overflow (you can see from the photographs that the swimming pool is level with the surround tiling and overflows into a collection gully around the swimming pool perimeter, which is concealed with a PVC grating). It was designed with two filters and three pumps, to give a 45 minute filtration cycle.

The capacity of this swimming pool, factoring in the balance tank, was about $30m^3$ (or 30,000 litres of water), which meant the filters and pumps had to deliver (or pump) $40m^3$ of water per hour.

To give the best possible water filtration quality, it is ideal to slow the water passing through the filtration media (fine sands and gravels) and this is achieved by making the surface area of the filtration bed as large as possible. In simple terms the larger the bed, the less amount of water gets pumped through and this is measurable in m^3 (flow rate) per m^2 (surface area) per hour. For example if one pumps $40m^3$ of water over $1m^2$ of filter media per hour, the filtration rate is in fact $40m^3/m^2/hour$. If a much bigger filter is fitted which has a $2m^2$ surface area of filter media, using the same pump and same example, the filtration rate will drop to a slower $20m^3/m^2/hour$.

It is not always possible to increase the size of the filter due to cost and physical space restrictions. Furthermore, to achieve a filter bed size of $2m^2$, the filter itself would be about 1600mm diameter, 2000mm in height and weigh about 5 tonnes! Having said this, it is possible to use 'deep bed filters' which, whilst they don't decrease the filtration rate, do enhance the filtration quality by virtue of having additional layers of media in these taller than normal filters.

Referring back to our example, $40m^3/m^2/hour$ filtration is considered high rate filtration and is usually deployed on the domestic back garden pool. Although not the best possible filtration rate, the compact filter and high performance pump will achieve the required turnover rate for an outdoor swimming pool (about 6 hours) and deliver reasonable quality swimming pool water, in a cost effective manner. $30m^3/m^2/hour$ and lower is medium filtration and would usually be seen in public and hotel swimming pools. Less than this, and getting down to $20m^3/m^2/hour$, is very desirable and is what we would aim for on hydrotherapy pools.

PROJECT 'BORDON'

The hydrotherapy swimming pool at Bordon special school was required to achieve these turnover rates, so a pump or pumps of 40m³/hour would be necessary; the size and specification of the filter were yet to be designed. We decided on two filters 1000mm in diameter, with a 1200mm (deep) bed of filter media. Combined with each filter was a 17m³/hour pump which gave us an excellent filtration rate of about 23m³/m²/hour. We also fitted a third pump, which meant that two pumps could always run if one failed, maintaining full circulation, or during periods of little or no use (nights or holiday periods) it would be feasible to run one pump and one filter, which would achieve a one and a half turnover period for the pool.

One important thing to note is that the lower the filtration, the more likely it is a second pump will be needed to achieve a proper backwash cycle (the process of reversing the flow of pool water through the filter bed to dislodge and disturb built up debris in the top of the filter media and discharge to waste via public drainage and sewers). At Bordon, the twin pump/twin filter set up allowed it to run at a low filtration rate for the higher quality hydrotherapy pool water, but also allowed us to use two pumps on one filter to give the filter a proper backwash and media scour.

When designing such a system, it is vital to ensure the filter selected will cope with a filtration rate of 50m³/m²/hour (which pressurises the filter vessel to the maximum limits). The existing or new mains drainage will cope with (in the case of Bordon) 36m³/hour of water for ten minutes (or 6000 litres of water being pushed down the drains) and one must be aware that backwashing one of the filters will dump about a quarter of the pool water – so consideration must be given to only backwashing at night, allowing the pool to refill and reheat and also backwashing only one filter at one time.

Once the filters and pumps are designed, the next selection to make is the type of disinfection that is required. It is always prudent to analyse the incoming town's water supply in order to take an overview on the compatibility with selected disinfectants and pH adjusters, to ensure there are no surprises in terms of dosing, for instance dosing alkali chemicals into high alkali water. Therefore, for this project it was specified that sulphuric acid be used to adjust Ph and that sodium hypochlorite would be used as the primary disinfectant (liquid chlorine) being the most effective disinfectant available. However, it would be run at the lowest possible levels, because a large commercial UV unit was to be fitted.

For hydrotherapy swimming pools it is essential that chemical levels in the pool flatline and do not oscillate, therefore automatic chemical monitoring and adjustment is almost a prerequisite of this swimming pool type. It is also not feasible to hand dose sulphuric acid and liquid chlorine into the swimming pool water, which has all sorts of associated health and safety and manual handling issues.

We therefore installed an automatic chemical dosing system with microprocessor control, which maintained the pool water with chlorine at about 1.5ppm, which seems a little high considering the ultra violet as well, but bacteria likes warm water and this pool is run between 34°C and 36°C. The commercial grade stainless steel bodied ultra violet disinfection lamp works in tandem with the automated chemical dosing and high specification filtration, to ensure that the users of this hydrotherapy pool enjoy the best possible water quality and bathing experience.

PROJECT 'BORDON'

Project 'Rose' in Southampton was a very similar hydrotherapy swimming pool, designed and constructed to a similar specification in the early 2000's.

This particular hydrotherapy swimming pool (as do most) had to cater for severely physically and mentally impaired clients, mostly of a young age. As well as fully considering the filtration, disinfection and heating systems to cope with both patient and hydrotherapist being in the pool water for long periods of time, the pool designer also needs to consider the physical elements such as safe entry and exit, into and out of the pool. Considerations must include whether a hoist may be required to lower patients with mobility impairment into the pool water (the hydrotherapists would be unable to carry out this task safely), how many steps are needed, whether a ramp access is needed, how are the step edges and edge of the pool, change in level defined or highlighted, whether the pool floor needs to be anti slip, the inclusion of handrails, handgrip and so on.

PROJECT 'ROSE'

Part of the brief for project 'Rose' highlighted the fact that many of the planned users of the hydrotherapy pool would suffer from poor sight. In the 5m x 4m hydrotherapy swimming pool, Guncast designed a flight of stairs against one short wall of the pool, which had an unusual quantity of steps with short risers, enabling gentle access into the pool water. The steps were tiled with a 'grip' mosaic in a different colour to the main body of the pool, and benefitted from a specially made long stainless steel handrail.

Although both project 'Rose' and project 'Bordon' were fitted with electronic powered patient hoists, the pool stairs at project 'Rose' enabled the mobile but less firm patients to enter and exit the pool water of their own accord, which is clearly a desirable feature. Project 'Rose' was a split water level hydrotherapy pool, which is slightly unusual – but had a shallow half of the pool of about 1000mm water depth and then a step down to a lower water level of 1150mm. This enables hydrotherapy for the young and old, but posed a problem on how to highlight the change in level. We decided to tile this in canary yellow mosaic to really stand out through the pool water, allowing everyone to see the step.

PROJECT ROSE

The hydrotherapy swimming pool, in its purist sense, is a swimming pool for the treatment of patients, which means that the filtration and disinfection system and the practicalities and usability of the pool for the patient is paramount. This must therefore be factored into the design over and above the pool's appearance. Most of these types of swimming pools are not the most beautiful, but are always (when designed properly) hygienic, safe and pleasant environments.

However, the general philosophy of well being or 'wellness' associated with hydrotherapy and water treatments, coupled with the ability of swimming pool designers and contractors to construct these high specification hydrotherapy swimming pools, led to the development of the vitality pool.

Since the mid 2000's, using technology and knowledge derived from the building of hydrotherapy swimming pools, swimming pool designers have been offering similar specification swimming pools but much crisper designed vitality pools, to the leisure and wellness sector.

Project 'Captain' was our first foray into building this type of vitality swimming pool (really before the term vitality swimming pool had been coined). A boutique hotel on the south coast of England required a small swimming pool which could be used for spa hydrotherapy, counter-current swimming against powerful jets, water aerobics and general relaxation.

Guncast was given a blank canvas in terms of swimming pool specification and design, but we were restricted to a pool size of no more than 6.5m x 4m. I found inspiration whilst on a family holiday in the Middle East where I saw a circular black marble water feature, probably about 3m in diameter. It gently filled and dispersed water evenly on all sides, being perfectly level, but the water on top looked still and reflective.

PROJECT 'CAPTAIN'

My design for the swimming pool was really focused around this idea of water dispersing evenly all the way around a raised black pool. At the time I described this look as an 'ultra level' swimming pool, as the water when still, was exactly level and due to the black mosaic lining, looked like a floating pane of glass.

Although aesthetically the concept for project 'Captain' was going to be stunning, we still had to provide a number of features within the swimming pool to enable all the uses the hotel required, keeping the water hygienic and also ensuring users could access the pool safely.

Firstly we took the view that, although larger than a spa, due to the running temperatures and medium to high levels of bathers, we should design the filtration system as if it were a spa. The full capacity of the swimming pool was 26m³ and we wanted a maximum 20 minute turnover resulting in large bore pipework to / from the pool and balance tank, two 1200mm deep bed filters and two 2.2kw circulation pumps, to achieve our target performance. We of course combined this high level of filtration quality with ozone disinfection and automated chemical dosing.

As the swimming pool was raised out of the floor level and overflowed, there was a perimeter collection gully (the same system as a deck level swimming pool) concealed under black pvc deck level grating, all feeding back to an underground balance tank just outside the building as there was no space internally. This specification of filtration and disinfection enabled the hotel to use the ultra level swimming pool at a variety of water temperatures, up to 36°C should they choose to do so, in the safe knowledge that the pool water will always be properly sanitised.

Next we had to provide the features.

During the design phase, we proposed to the hotel that about one third of the pool should be segregated by a dividing wall, with a central opening to the main section of the pool and at a shallower level. This was to be the seated spa end, providing seating and hydro air jets for ten bathers, with seats to the long and two short walls.

The seat was diamond drilled through the black mosaic, forming eighty 5mm diameter air bubble outlets. These provide a gentle aerated water movement behind the bather's back.

The spa area, being shallower and built with a seat, became the access point by way of a fitted handrail and a concrete tiled step onto the lower spa seat.

PROJECT 'CAPTAIN'

The main section of the pool was 1200mm water depth - deep enough for water aerobics - and was fitted with two counter-current swim jets at the far end, so bathers can actually swim against the current in the smaller than normal pool.

Overall the concept of the overflowing ultra level pool was a success and the hotel was extremely pleased to own such an unusual looking 'vitality' pool with so many features fitted into a pool of this size.

Robert Wilson, Director of the hotel comments:

"I remember you very well even from day one when we came along to your barn for our very first chat. The Spa as a business is doing really well and people are still 'wowed' by it all."

PROJECT 'CAPTAIN'

Following on from the early success of project 'Captain' and as we progressed and pushed design boundaries, vitality pools have become much more common and require higher specifications.

Whilst the original vitality pools featured extremely good quality filtration and disinfection, this has not changed too dramatically since the early designs. What has changed is the type of features fitted into the vitality pools and the materials used.

Project 'Captain' was lined internally with an anthracite black glass mosaic with black grout which gave it a unique 'mirror like' appearance when the water was still. It was fitted throughout with stainless steel pool fittings and a concrete tiled spa seating area. A more modern approach would be to line the pool interior with large porcelain tiles, dark or beige and have the seating or benches formed from polished stainless steel tubing, which have bubble pads fitted underneath or stand up bubble stations with jets or bubbles massaging the bather's torso. Large neck massage jets with powerful streams of water or curtains of water for bathers to stand in are also popular.

Working alongside filtration experts Barr & Wray, Guncast constructed such a vitality swimming pool at project 'Stanley', which is a luxury hotel overlooking the Ribble Valley in Lancashire, North England.

PROJECT 'STANLEY'

The pool itself is 6mx 4.5m and overflows on two sides (to a balance tank), overlooking the Ribble Valley through the pool hall wall-to-floor windows. The swimming pool, pool hall surround and pool edging are all finished with beige textured 600mm x 300mm Italian porcelain tiles, which flow seamlessly from one to another and give the pool water a bluey green relaxing hue.

The whole pool is fitted with colour change LED underwater lights so that the colour of the water can be altered to various mood settings, for example purple/red for invigorating or blue for cool and relaxing.

From the photographs of this project you can clearly see the stainless hydrobac immersed bench, which is the full width of the swimming pool and can easily seat six bathers side by side. This type of unit is fabricated off site and positioned and bolted down into the swimming pool structure.

Air blowers in the pool plant room blow air through pipes positioned under the seat to emit air bubbles evenly along the bench. The neck massage spouts and bubble station, which are activated by infra red detectors when the bather enters the feature area, can also be seen in the photographs.

When activated, the neck massage spout blasts a jet of water so that the bather can position their neck or head under the water for a powerful massage, whilst the bubble station massages the torso using the sixteen positioned air and water massage jets around the tiled massage station. Often the massage stations are also formed off site in stainless steel – but on this occasion we decided to use facetted porcelain in keeping with the tiling concept.

"Vitality pool built in association with Barr & Wray - leading experts in filtration."

PROJECT 'STANLEY'

6m x 5m x 1.2m deep Italian porcelain clad with infinity edges to two sides over looking the Ribble Valley

Two swan neck massage stations

One massage station formed in facetted porcelain with sixteen mini massage jets

Stainless steel hydro massage bench to one wall of pool with bubble outlets

Project 'Stanley' encompasses all aspects of the hydrotherapy pool's high quality filtration and usability points, but includes the modern day leisure add-ons that make it a vitality pool for 'wellness'.

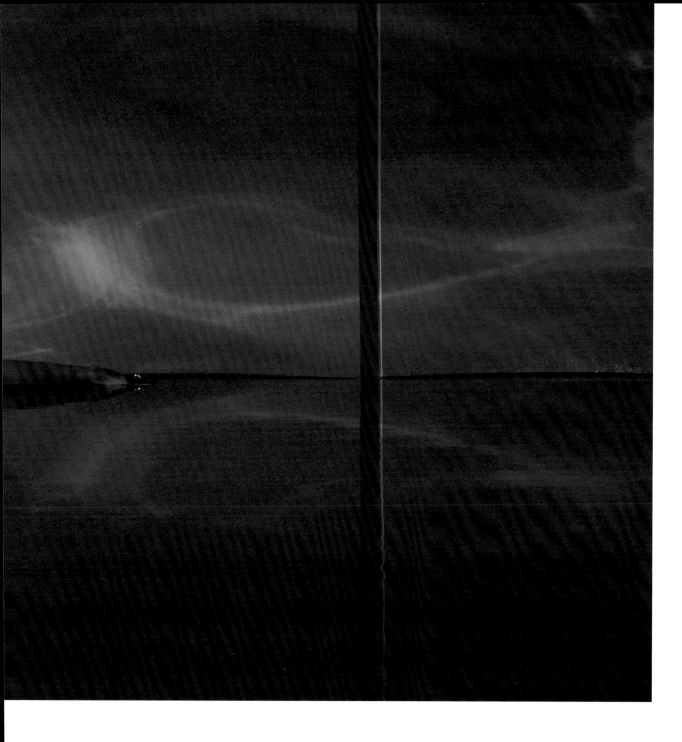

Hydrotherapy in one form or another has existed for many years. The basic premise is that generally humans like bathing and find water massage and warm water exercise both therapeutic and reinvigorating.

I believe that hydrotherapy swimming pools will continue to exist as a method of treatment for various ailments and leisure vitality swimming pools will continue to thrive and push the boundaries of design and available features.

chapter 9

'PRIVATE MEMBERS CLUBS'

Pre 1980's in the UK, for the serious swimmer wanting to swim distance, the only option would have been to go to the local swimming pool or 'baths' to swim in the 20m or 25m long swimming pool. Even to this day swimming pools longer than 25m are surprisingly few within the UK. 50m pools do exist but even when including the large lido pools, there are still only around thirty, of which only ten or twelve are fully open to the public and comply to the measured Olympic standard 50m pool size.

Although a large proportion of the older, bigger municipal swimming pools were falling into disrepair in the 1990's and 2000's and were also considered uneconomic to run, the UK's successful 2012 summer Olympic bid added momentum to refurbishing these older swimming pools and developing new facilities.

Guncast was involved with one such community project. 25m swimming pool project 'Highworth' had fallen into disrepair during the 1990's. The local community formed an 'action fundraising committee' with the sole goal of saving the local swimming pool facility.

Over a period of about 10 years, the funds were raised to completely refurbish the swimming pool, making it into a compliant 25m swimming pool (in terms of measured length), providing a 3m diving platform, and enclosing the pool with a glazed building (the old swimming pool was an outdoor swimming pool).

During 2007 / 2008 the work was carried out and Guncast's role was to supply and install the new filtration system, comprising of pool fittings and underwater lighting, new pool circulation pipework, air handling unit, filters pumps and chemical dosing system.

Whilst project 'Highworth' was a success for all involved and the new facility was enjoyed by many, since the late 1980's / early 1990's the municipal swimming pool has contended with funding and refurbishment issues, but also gaps were spotted in the market - new pressures were developing from the private sector with the advent of health clubs and centres starting to offer 25m indoor and outdoor swimming pools and spas.

The business model for these health clubs was that an individual or a family pay a monthly membership fee, for which access into the club and all the facilities are available. The clubs were orientated around a swimming pool and gym, but often included racket sports as well.

PROJECT 'HIGHWORTH '

One of the early and most successful pioneers of racket and fitness clubs, which included indoor and outdoor swimming pools, were the 'David Lloyd' centres.

As far as Guncast was concerned, each club was to include an indoor swimming pool (ideally 25m, dependant on space restrictions) a spa and an outdoor pool 20m or 25m.

The first indoor pools we built for the clubs in the early 1990's tended to be shaped or freeform. However, through the club's internal marketing and research they established that firstly the swimming pool facility was very high on the client's wish list and secondly the pools should be long and suitable for lane training.

Two of the very early indoor swimming pools we built in the London area clubs, we subsequently remodelled into rectangular 25m pools. Throughout the 1990's we completed around twenty swimming pool projects for the 'David Lloyd' clubs – all based on the same successful formula.

While David Lloyd (and other health clubs with swimming pools) rapidly expanded during this period, it became evident that there was a massive public appetite for the private members club that included a swimming pool. This phenomenon was not just restricted to the UK as similar traits were seen across Europe and Australia. Competition was born and unique selling points were needed.

Luxury boutique hotels and exclusive retreats needed their swimming pool facilities to sell their private memberships, not just to transient clients but also to local users. This drove the quality and design of the swimming pool upward.

'DAVID LLOYD' PROJECTS

Project 'Cowshed' was an indoor swimming pool built into an existing cattle barn in the grounds of a stately home. The property had been purchased by an entrepreneur, who converted it into a rural extension of their private members club in central London. The project, which was completed in the mid 1990s, also featured a 20m outdoor swimming pool, which extended away from the cow barn in an elevated position, allowing us to build four gun slit glazed viewing windows into the pool wall.

The concept behind the overall project was that it had to be unique, high quality and designer in appearance. This was client driven, as the retreat had to be in harmony with their exclusive London club and be attractive for their existing clients to travel down and spend time at the new property.

With this in mind, the swimming pools were designed in a contemporary fashion. The indoor swimming pool had to be formed within the confines of the existing cow barn for planning reasons. This meant the final size of the pool wasn't established until the underpinning was completed. This is because underpinning foundations can deviate from the wall line underneath, causing concrete to protrude slightly, which obviously the swimming pool structure cannot pass through.

The final size of the indoor pool ended up around 15m long by 4m wide, leaving a minimal walkway down one side of the pool, in order to maximise the pool size.

The outdoor swimming pool had no space limitations but was built at the same floor level as the indoor pool so bathers could walk from one to the other. However, the ground level dropped away very quickly and, although the furthest end from the barn was to be a 2m deep end (which corresponded to the way the land levels dropped away from the barn), the underside of the deep end of the swimming structure was still effectively out of the ground. We therefore had to excavate away the top soil and use large quantities of ready mixed concrete to form a foundation for the swimming pool structure to sit on.

A further complication was that although one side of the swimming pool was completely out of the ground (hence the viewing windows), the opposite side would have been also, until built up with surround slab for sunbathing / sitting. Building regulations stipulated this must be strong enough to support a fire engine so that the swimming pool could be used as a reservoir in case of a fire. This meant that the swimming pool structure had to support a suitable structural slab and in turn the pool wall seriously enhanced with additional steel and concrete to act as a cantilever support wall to hold up the surround slab. So the outdoor swimming pool on the face of it may look like a straight forward build, but it was actually very structurally demanding.

Both pools are lined throughout with a 50mm x 50mm matt black Portuguese mosaic and both pools were deck level with a stainless steel perimeter edge grating, which at the time (to my knowledge) had not been done before. The elevated section of the outdoor pool, with its gun slit windows, overlooked a meadow and onward to a small lake.

Project 'Limewood' was a similar concept in terms of being a luxury retreat, but was completed nearly two decades after project 'Cowshed'. I would argue quite strongly that the swimming pools and vitality pools built into these later boutique retreats were not so much inspired by the earlier projects, but were driven forward into higher and higher specifications, bespoke features and crisp design.

Project 'Limewood' consisted of a 20m x 8m indoor deck level swimming pool. The pool was lined throughout in various sizes of pre-cut light green slate porcelain. The walls of the pool were random size porcelain, whilst the pool floor was 600mm x 300mm with a border around the floor perimeter of 600mm x 100mm strips. The deck level edge system was stainless steel with in-laid porcelain tiles so that no stainless steel can be seen, other than two continuous linear 8mm gaps all the way round the pool perimeter at surround slab level. The pool water percolates over the pool wall, through the 8mm linear gaps and into the collection channel below, then onward to the balance tank. Gone are the days of a blue mosaic 'commercial pool' with white plastic PVC deck level grating!

PROJECT 'LIMEWOOD'

The sleek modern indoor pool was complemented with an indoor vitality pool, approximately 8m x 6m, with one of the 6m walls curved and an infinity edge overlooking the herb garden and outdoor steaming spa. The pool was lined throughout with light green slate porcelain as per the main pool, but fitted with two stainless steel air loungers, two stainless steel bubble stand up massage stations and stainless steel neck massagers. All of these bespoke stainless steel vitality pool features were specially made and fitted by Barr & Wray and are a huge attraction. The pool is run at 36°C, so not quite spa temperatures, but extremely warm for relaxing.

Not content with just indoor pools, the owner commissioned an outdoor spa pool as well. Guncast designed and built a very large 3m x 3m outdoor spa pool, sited in the middle of the adjacent herb garden. With profiled seating comfortably for twelve bathers, including hydro air jets, seat bubbles and central air bath volcano, the outdoor spa pool was a real hit. Due to the sloping and rounded seating, we tiled the spa throughout with bottle green glass mosaic, in keeping with the internal pools' colour schemes.

PROJECT 'LIMEWOOD'

Of course the all-encompassing term 'private members club', which includes luxury retreats and boutique hotels, could also include school pools, of which we have been involved with many over the past four decades.

One unusual project, which was almost a hybrid of a school pool and a private members club, was project 'Dragon Play'.

An upmarket crèche in South London, which provided day and after school care for children of working parents, found a niche offering much more than the normal crèche. For example, a mixture of learning facilities such as cooking and a library of books, one-to-one tuition, combined with play facilities like indoor golf, computer games and home cinema. The owners were looking to open a flagship crèche to add to its existing excellent facilities. The new crèche was to be on a first floor in a new build block of luxury apartments and to include a 15m 'children's swimming pool'.

There were two major challenges to overcome. Firstly, whilst the apartment block was new build, it was, in fact, built and occupied. The swimming pool was on a first floor over a basement car park, but the existing structure had not been built to support the weight of a swimming pool, nor had it been built utilising waterproof concrete.

The second challenge to overcome was that the client wanted a very high specification swimming pool with excellent water quality for young children, warm water (33°C), an unusual tiling scheme and a beach area with water play features.

Firstly we had to deal with the swimming pool structural weight and the waterproofing issue, as even though we intended to waterproof the pool to the highest possible degree, it is generally accepted that small quantities of water can escape even the most watertight structures and can build up to cause a damp issue.

PROJECT 'DRAGON PLAY'

Not only was the existing structural slab technically not strong enough to support the pool, the 2m commercial filter (to achieve water turnover of one hour) when charged with media and full of water was also too heavy.

We circumnavigated the filter issue by placing the filter on steels, which spread the weight over a larger area of floor slab. This resulted (unfortunately) in locating the filter in the centre of the plant room, resulting in an unusually laid out plant room – but the problem was dealt with.

Next, the structural issue. It transpired that the main body of the pool was on a bearing which would take the pool weight when full of water, but the area of concern was the beach area with the play features (which essentially are stainless steel spray nozzles or jets attached to cast-in header units). Each spray unit (of which there were six) had a cast-in header unit which was designed to sit in a block of concrete. The block of concrete and the surrounding pool structure were simply too heavy for the bearing zone that the beach area was sitting on. We devised a system of stainless strutting bolted to each header unit and bolted to the existing structural slab, which in turn passed through our structure. The whole swimming pool structure (including the beach area) was therefore designed to be as thin as possible, to mitigate the weight issue.

The method of supporting the play features posed another problem. As the concrete of the beach area was now only 200mm thick, this would leave a void under the beach. This was overcome by laying down light weight extruded polystyrene void packers, which provided a formation base for the concrete structure.

PROJECT 'DRAGON PLAY'

Structural issues overcome, we now turned our attention to waterproofing, especially in the area which was peppered with the penetrations for the play features. Conventional waterproof render was applied and then a high grade waterproofing system with meshing, which wraps around the pipework and penetrations, called Mapelastic made by Mapei.

Once applied and before tiling the pool, we water tested the pool and left it full for a period of time to monitor and check that it was not leaking, which was the case. For minor seepage and any condensation that could build up behind the pool structure, we laid a waterproof membrane under the pool and were able to tap into drainage downpipes around the pool which fed into the basement underneath. A series of drainage points around the pool structure collect any build up of water and feeds it into the down pipes.

The pool was lined with different coloured tiles to create a very unusual and unique looking swimming pool which, within the confines of a 'private members children club', works wonderfully.

Although the air in the pool hall (which has to be one degree hotter than the pool water) is very warm and would be uncomfortably hot in normal clothes, for the children playing in the beach area, spray features and water tunnel (which are activated via push buttons in the beach area), it is an ideal temperature.

Completed in 2012, 'Dragon Play' was a particularly challenging but very satisfying project as it is, and will be, used and enjoyed by many children.

With a trend in London toward luxury apartment living (as with the apartments fully occupied above project 'Dragon Play'), we have recently seen an incorporation into these apartment blocks of communal health suites, which include a swimming pool and spa, again typically constructed above the garaging.

The ability to incorporate swimming pools and spas into this type of building has led Guncast into the market place for the construction of such projects. Like the upward trend in specification that we have seen over the last two decades, these pools are now being highly specified, designer in appearance and must befit the luxury apartment lifestyle living.

PROJECT 'DRAGON PLAY'

Typically long term builds (as huge building sites are), project 'Reach' is a project we were awarded when writing this book and will be completed in 2014.

The indoor 15m swimming pool and large hydro spa pool, with large sauna and steam room, are all part of our remit and when it is completed will be one of the newest, most up-to-date, most cutting edge 'private members' swimming pools in London.

PROJECT 'REACH'

chapter 10

'FUTURISM'

Throughout the course of the previous chapters and the various case studies, the focus has been on completed projects that are special in one way or another, forming the basis for future swimming pool projects, in terms of pushing the boundaries of design.

This chapter will showcase projects that are at the cutting edge of design (at the time of writing this book), and by looking at these we see what the swimming pools of the future will look like!

Project 'Bathe and Bubble' was commissioned circa 2010 for clients who wanted to demolish their existing home and rebuild a new property on the same site. The property was to be extremely modern, not only in appearance but also in technology and was to include a 15m x 3m infinity edge indoor lap pool. The client intended for the new house to be low energy and, being from a technology background himself, was extremely hands on. He designed the house management system that monitored all the heating and electrical plant and ensured that it was running as per the energy conscious design, which included heat derived from solar panels and a ground source heat pump system.

The combination of solar and ground source 'green energy' was boosted by air to water heat pumps, which provide low thermal hot water in the region of 55°C. This is sufficient to provide the heat resource needed for an air handling unit, which heats the pool water and pool hall air.

Although the use of a combination of energy sources is not uncommon and is described as an 'energy centre', what we do not see at present is this combined approach being used to its full capability. With the appetite for fossil fuels fading as resources diminish, and the concern for carbon emissions becoming more and more topical, the drive towards using energy in this manner will become more mainstream.

To build an energy centre in a new build property is an expensive operation, but does have vision. My personal view is, as the capital cost of installing this type of equipment drops and the kit itself becomes more efficient, more and more swimming pools will feature low energy heating options and multi speed pumps that do not run full bore at all times and will feature a low speed or set back mode to save electrical consumption. Obviously this is not a ground breaking statement, but it is important to consider where the electricity comes from to power an air source heat pump, for example.

The swimming pool owner may well be saving electricity by heating their pool via an air source heat pump, but if the electricity itself is coming from a coal fired power station it almost defeats the object. We will see a trend toward domestic environs not only using less energy but, by becoming more energy self sufficient (we have already been involved with a number of projects that included a wind turbine to provide a proportion of electricity), ultimately we will see changes at national grid level which will mirror the energy centres and ethos behind them, pioneered by clients such at these.

PROJECT 'BATHE AND BUBBLE'

The clients not only wanted to create an energy efficient property, as close as possible to carbon neutral, but were also heavily focused on future proofing the design for themselves and generations to come. Whilst every component in the house, including the swimming pool, was carefully selected, the clients also had an unforgiving eye for detail and accuracy. Every product had to be of the highest quality but also installed and fitted with no deviation from its design location and specification.

The property and swimming pool had an ultra-modern design in appearance. The swimming pool was to be a lap pool (15m x 3m x 1.2m water depth) and infinity edge to one long side and one short side. The pool features an automatic pool cover at one end, hidden in a wall housing recess behind some tiled removable PVC facia panels and supported by a stainless steel support frame. The pool was tiled internally with tiny white iridescent 10mm x 10mm mosaic that shimmered with colour when the pool was filled with water. Black basalt tiles were used around the pool.

To make matters slightly more complicated for us, the clients (who had been on a recent trip to Switzerland) had been staying in a hotel with a luxury swimming pool complex, which included some underwater stainless steel benches with bubble pads underneath. Having enjoyed relaxing in these bubble benches, they decided to include a similar stainless steel bench in their own pool. The real complication was where to locate such a bench and bubble pad. The two ends of the pool were occupied by steps at one end and access panels to cover the pool cover system at the other, which would impede swimming laps, and fitting the bench to one side of the pool would do the same (as the pool is only 3m wide).

After a lot of discussion and introducing Teemu Griffiths of Hydrofloors (specialist in stainless steel fabrication and mechanisation of swimming pool moving floors) to the project, it was decided that a 2m long stainless steel tubular bench would be fixed to two water based hydraulic rams. These would push and pull the bench out of a housing in the pool wall side.

We constructed a housing under the basalt to one side of the swimming pool, which was set back enough and wide enough to accommodate the stainless bench in its entirety once retracted, with the rams also inside the pool water. The rams were powered by a power pack sited in the plant room, which uses water based hydraulics (oil is not compatible with pool water!). When activated, the rams slowly push the bench into the up position, profiled for the bather to lie comfortably on.

Set into the mosaic under the bench (in the up position) we were also asked to fabricate and fit a stainless steel bubble pad. Teemu designed a stainless steel 'box' which was about 2m x 1m (x 90mm in depth) and had predrilled bubble outlets (two hundred 5mm diameter holes), which were connected to two 3hp air blowers. When the blowers are turned on, a large plume of air erupts under the bench to give a vigorous air massage to the bathers on the bench (which comfortably sits two). Cleverly, the clients wanted the bench in the retracted mode to slightly protrude from its housing at the top, so the top stainless steel tube could double up as a handrail to hold onto when standing on the bubble pad whilst the air is blowing.

PROJECT 'BATHE AND BUBBLE'

As a concept, the retractable bench is a brilliant idea and, now installed, it works to perfection. However, the research and development that goes into such a product is not to be under estimated. Teemu had to consider the mechanical engineering. The bench could not twist, bounce, or pull out of the wall, but also had to be profiled correctly for seating and the final positions of the bench in the up or down position were critical. Before we started creating the bench, Teemu and I travelled to Switzerland to examine the bench that inspired the client and subsequently made a prototype for approval. We felt this was essential in order to deliver to the clients exactly what was in their minds.

Controlling the bench became quite complex as neither the bench, nor the bubble pad could be operated when the pool cover was on. Interlocks were required to prevent that from happening. The bubble pad and bench required controls that were stylish and watertight and, of course, emergency stops, in case the bench was operated at the wrong time. As with all research and development, it is not always possible to pass on fully the costs incurred to the client, but what it does, is form a font of knowledge for future projects, and creates ability within your own team to deliver all sorts of aspirational swimming pools of the future.

Teemu Griffiths of Hydrofloors comments:

"I received a telephone call from Guncast in Brussels requesting a meeting in London (first thing the next morning) concerning a moving stainless steel bench. Intrigued by the challenge I decided to travel that evening.

Upon meeting Jack Harding, the client and the design team in the morning, it was clear the client had very clear visions on how the bench would work mechanically and had already carried out some calculations, intending to use a ball screw system to wind the stainless steel bench in and out of its wall housing; which we had at that time pre tested but had failed under water. After prolonged discussion we agreed on the principal that the bench would operate on two 63mm diameter rams, powered by a water based hydraulic power pack. Jack and I subsequently travelled to Switzerland to measure and replicate the seat in a swimming pool in a luxury hotel that had inspired the client.

My mechanical engineers were set to work at Hydrofloors, the research and development undertaken, prototypes fabricated. Once all were approved by the client, the final product - a moving bench that powers in and out of a swimming pool wall - was installed with functions as specified by the client. The challenges that Guncast and their clients have posed to me and my team over the years have been relished and have allowed us to build a portfolio of unique projects."

'Bathe and Bubble' was possibly one of the most challenging projects Guncast has ever completed. The client was extremely meticulous and demanding (quite rightly so – they were building their dream 'future proof' house), but in many ways it was one of the most rewarding swimming pools we have been involved with.

PROJECT 'BATHE AND BUBBLE'

Working with Hydrofloors on other futuristic projects included a number of moving floor projects, but only one moving wall!

Project 'Otter' was commissioned in 2010 and completed about one year later. The project was a full refurbishment of a large plot of land, which dropped away from the house quite steadily.

Although the main dwelling was a refurbishment, the scope of works included an extension to the side of the property, to incorporate a 20m long swimming pool, which was partly indoor and partly outdoor. The width of the pool was 4m and the depth in the indoor section 1m – 1.5m; the outdoor pool was 1.5m to 2.3m, making the outdoor section of the swimming pool deep enough for diving. In fact, we did also fit a diving board.

Again, being a domestic project, the client expected an extremely elegant and well designed swimming pool, so the pool had to look good as well as function properly and feature a moving wall. The moving wall would lift from the swimming pool floor, rise up and divide the outdoor section of the pool from the indoor section.

In the first instance specifying and designing the filtration and heating system for a combined indoor and outdoor swimming pool is not straight forward. The pool needs to be treated as one body of water, but the demands for heating and chemically treating an outdoor swimming pool are completely different to an indoor swimming pool. The way to tackle this conundrum, is to regard the pool as one, as a design for the most onerous scenario.

In short, the heating loads must be specified as if the whole pool is outdoor and the chlorine levels run as if the pool is outdoor (sunlight will erode the chlorine levels quicker on an outdoor swimming pool). Good circulation and a high turnover rate, coupled with automated chemicals is desirable (as the chemical adjustment will be more accurate and more responsive), thus maintaining quality swimming conditions throughout.

PROJECT 'OTTER'

Guncast specified two filters and two pumps so that it would be feasible to run the indoor swimming pool throughout the year, but allow the heating to be turned off and the filtration to be turned down (to, say, a few hours per day) on the outdoor swimming pool at the same time. It will never be possible to completely isolate the indoor swimming water from the outdoor swimming pool.

Water will make its way round the moving wall and the outdoor pool will share heat and chemical treatment with the indoor pool, which is a good thing but needs to be considered in terms of running cost. Even if the partition between the two pools was 100% watertight, heat would still transfer through the fabric of the partition.

Project 'Otter' was designed in the knowledge that heat would transfer to the outdoor swimming pool water if the outdoor swimming pool was 'turned off', or if the outdoor swimming pool would be heated throughout the year. Either way, it made sense to fit a solar gain slatted automatic pool cover to minimise heat loss. This was fitted under the decking positioned underneath the diving board, beneath removable timber decking panels and supported on a stainless steel frame.

Guncast commissioned Hydrofloors to design and install a stainless steel moving wall that could be tiled as per the pool (which in this case was an Italian greeny / grey glass mosaic with matching grout). The wall was fabricated in the same way as a moving floor; in other words the wall was filled with buoyancy packs and floats up to its correct position, anchored by a stainless steel chain. This was powered by the same motor as the slatted automatic pool cover, which pushes or pulls the wall up and down via a stainless steel worm drive, discreetly set into a stainless steel runner in the pool wall. The pool wall measured 300mm thick once tiled, and is very sturdy. As well as dividing one pool from the other, it needs to prevent unwanted intruders from accessing the house.

To complement the scheme, the client and his architect commissioned mechanised glass 'doors' which spanned over the moving wall. When operated, two glazed panels (each 2m wide and about 2.5m in height) pull apart and swing open to reveal the indoor pool to the outdoor pool and the landscaped gardens beyond.

The door, the moving wall, the pool cover and the underwater lighting are all controlled by a mini control panel designed by Guncast and fitted into the pool hall. The whole concept of being able to push a button and watch a pool wall drop away, while simultaneously the glazing above swings apart to reveal a 20m indoor / outdoor swimming pool, is futuristic and offers the best of both worlds. No doubt it will not be the last time Guncast will design and build a swimming pool like this, to add to our portfolio.

PROJECT 'OTTER'

Swimming pools of the future are not always based around new technology. For me, architecture is an extremely important ingredient.

Completed in 2013, project 'Stones' was a two phase build, of which the second phase was to include an indoor swimming pool. Guncast was appointed to design and construct the swimming pool by the revered architectural practice 'Yiangou Architects' and work alongside the main contractor, WG Carter – who specialise in large Cotswold property construction and new build.

Ander Inchley of Yiangou, in his own words, sets the scene:

"Yiangou Architects was commissioned in April 2010 to design a scheme that would consist of 2 phases. The first was to be the extension and renovation of a large, traditional Cotswold house that had previously been owned by the church and one of the Oxford colleges. The second phase, to commence as the renovation of the house completed, was the construction of a new pool and leisure building.

Given the client's background in precision engineering and cutting edge design, an early design decision was that the pool building should be a sleek, contemporary structure to contrast the rustic, traditionalism of the main house. To allow the pool to stand alone as a minimal and precise pavilion, all the mechanical equipment associated with an indoor swimming pool are housed in a separate garage building with all the cables and ducting tunnelled underground, rising up into the building in its solid end gable, whilst facilities such as the changing rooms, showers and gymnasium are all housed in a separate building, connected to the pool by a frameless, glass link. The link becomes almost invisible, maintaining the separation and individuality of the two buildings.

The Gym Building, as it became known, provides the transition between traditional house and contemporary pool building. The south side of the building, facing the main house, is constructed from Cotswold stone (largely reclaimed from the site) with narrow, barn-like slit windows and a large main entrance opening. However, the north side of the building is defined by its large, frameless glazed openings and horizontal cedar boarding; a more contemporary appearance and detailing, in a similar architectural language to the pool building."

PROJECT 'STONES'

Frameless sliding glass panels form the walls of the pool building. The pool can be opened right up to the gardens on a beautiful summer's day but the visual connections and feelings of being outside in amongst the gardens are still maintained when the English summer adopts its more usual, unpredictable nature and the screens are shut. To reinforce the connections between inside and out, the riven stone flooring of the pool surround runs flush, right out to the external terraces, with a rill flowing water from the far ends of the garden until it appears to run into the pool itself.

We wanted the pool to feel more like it was naturally formed, as opposed to the usual artificial bright blues and turquoise of the traditional swimming pool. So together with the riven grey stone pool surround slabs, greeny-black, slate-like tiles were used within the pool itself to create a dark, black pool with the feeling that you may never reach its bottom. The pool is lit with tiny fibre optic lights, to give just a faint glow at night whilst remaining unnoticeable when not in use.

However, the defining feature of the pool building is the ceiling. A curving structure, finished in a polished Venetian plaster; it has been designed to give the impression that the roof is floating, with the ceiling visually detached from the columns holding it all up. There are no lights piercing this sleek, smooth surface; hidden strips of tiny LEDs light the top section of ceiling, which appears to glow, light reflecting down off the polished plaster.

To ensure that the purity of the building was not diluted, every effort was made in the detailing to ensure that all grilles, switches, speakers, lights, alarms, detectors and control panels that come with modern living were either concealed entirely or designed in a way to ensure they remain unnoticed. We wanted this to be a place to retreat to and relax in, a serene environment with no distractions, where you lie relaxing in your dark, "bottomless" pool looking up at the curved, floating "sky" above.

For me the success of project 'Stones' was the architecture and material selection for the swimming pool and the pool surround tiling. It is for this reason I include it as a futuristic pool because, at the time of writing, although there are swimming pools that look similar, I see this swimming pool as very forward thinking in terms of its appearance.

PROJECT 'STONES'

There are subtleties in this design which, in my opinion, are simply sublime. The pool is lined with porcelain, which was carefully selected by the clients and is greeny-black and riven, so does look very much like a natural slate.

Rather than taking the risk of installing a natural stone inside the pool water, time was taken to explore all the possible materials available. (Natural material is often not compatible with pool water - and quite often when problems manifest themselves it is too late!) The pool edge stone is a very unusual detail in being centrally rebated on the pool edge face and the grey honed natural stone used for the coping and surround is not a material I have seen or used before; the colour complements the pool tiling and works well with the grey venetian plaster.

This attention to detail and time taken to select these materials not only makes for a successful project, but also sets the scene for how luxury indoor swimming pools will look in the future. Project 'Stones' appeals massively to my own personal tastes.

In recent years fibre optic lighting has been installed on the highest specification swimming pools as being the ultimate underwater lighting solution. As mentioned previously, the light source is accessible in the plant room, which generates light to be fed down fibre optic strands or cables into the light emitters in the pool water. The light generator is also able to colour change. Although this underwater lighting solution is not inexpensive, once installed it is extremely reliable; although a light generator bulb could blow, or the unit break down – this is easily fixable and does not require the pool to be drained or maintenance undertaken in the pool water.

PROJECT 'STONES'

Project 'Royale' included a client request for colour change fibre optic. The pool itself is relatively large for an indoor swimming pool (12m x 6m) and was tiled in a dark mosaic blend.

At that time, the scheme we designed and installed included three light generators, each feeding light down fibre optic cables to 3 sets of twelve light emitters housed in 70mm diameter stainless steel housings set into the pool wall.

With a total of 36 light emitters, we were able to feed light into the pool water at high and low level (in the deep end), into the spa pool and on to the steps. The effect was stunning and much enjoyed by the client.

PROJECT 'ROYALE'

Project 'Stones' was completed five or six years later than project 'Royale' and we can see how the fibre optic is still the optimum solution, but there has been a trend toward a more subtle underwater lighting affect. Each of the 80 light emitters at project 'Stones' are much smaller (about 15mm in diameter) and the overall effect is much gentler. Again, I see this as the underwater light scheme of the future, where the pool and the pool fittings are kept simple in design, and result in a sleek effect.

PROJECT 'ROYALE'

Designing and building swimming pools has been my life and has allowed me to meet some extremely interesting and successful people; and also to travel extensively. This has been made possible by the clients who commissioned our work and the dedicated team of people who work for Guncast, some of whom have worked for the company longer than I have.

All the time there are clients and customers who require a design focused swimming pool company that produces quality swimming pools, the future looks bright and exciting.

Jack Harding